Símbolos

Tendo em conta a grande diversidade de línguas faladas em
utilização de símbolos internacionais em lugar duma descriç
texto. Desta forma, podem-se obter facilmente as mais impo
todas as espécies e como delas cuidar.
Os símbolos utilizados para informar sobre como cuidar das espécies,
condições em aquário, e não às do país ou do biótopo de origem.

Continente de origem

Veja a letra correspondente diante do número de código

A = África
E = Europa
N = América do Norte
S = América Latina
X = Ásia + Austrália

Idade

o último algarismo do código indica a idade do peixe

1 = muito pequeno (cria/ juvenil pequeno)
2 = pequeno (juvenil/ tamanho vendável)
3 = médio (sub-adulto/ bom tamanho de venda)
4 = grande (adulto/ tamanho de criação)
5 = extra grande (adulto em tamanho máximo)
6 = excepcionalmente grande (espécime de exposição)

Origem

W = espécime selvagem-capturado na natureza
B = criação de cativeiro
X = forma híbrida
Z = forma cultivada (variedade seleccionada pelo homem)

Tamanho

... cm = tamanho aproximado em adulto

Sexo

♂ macho
♀ fêmea
♂♀ par

Temperatura

18–22°C (64–72°F) temperatura ambiente
22–25°C (72–77°F) a maioria dos peixes tropicais
24–29°C (75–85°F) Discus etc.
10–22°C (50–72°F) fria/ temperada; i.e. América do Norte/Europa)

Valor-pH

pH 6,5–7,2 sem necessidades especiais (neutro)
pH 5,8–6,5 prefere águas pouco duras, ligeiramente ácidas
pH 7,5–8,5 prefere águas duras, alcalinas

Iluminação

intensa, cheia de luz / sol
não muito intensa
muito suave

Alimentação

omnívoro: comida seca, sem necessidades especiais
alimentação especial: alimento vivo, alimento congelado
piscívoros: alimenta-se de peixes vivos
herbívoro: necessita de comida vegetal

Profundidade preferida

meia água/ todos os níveis de profundidade
nível superior/ peixe de superfície
nível inferior/peixe de fundo

Decoração do Aquário

somente rochas e areão
rochas e troncos de madeira, cavernas
plantas + rochas e troncos

Comportamento/ Reprodução

manter um par ou um trio
peixe de cardume. Mínimo aconselhável 10 peixes
ovíparo
vivíparo
incubador de boca
incubador de caverna
construtor de ninho de bolhas
comedor de algas/ limpa vidros
peixe sociável, fácil de manter (aquário comunitário)
difícil de manter, ler literatura específica antes de adquirir
atenção, extremamente difícil, somente para especialistas experimentados
os ovos requerem cuidados especiais
§ espécie protegida, (WA), requere licença especial (CITES)
~L~ anfíbio (necessita duma zona terrestre)
<Bw> água salobra
~Sw~ marinho (vive no mar)
<~Sw~ vive no mar enquanto juvenil (mais tarde quer em água salobra quer doce)
~Sw~> vive em água doce enquanto juvenil (mais tarde também em água salgada)
<~Sw~> vive quer em água salgada quer em água doce (varia!)

Aquário Mínimo

SS	mínimo	20–40 cm	5–20 l
S	pequeno	40–80 cm	40–80 l
m	médio	60–100 cm	80–200 l
L	grande	100–200 cm	200–400 l
XL	XL	200–400 cm	400–3 000 l
XXL	XXL	acima de 400 cm	acima de 3 000 l (aquário de exposição)

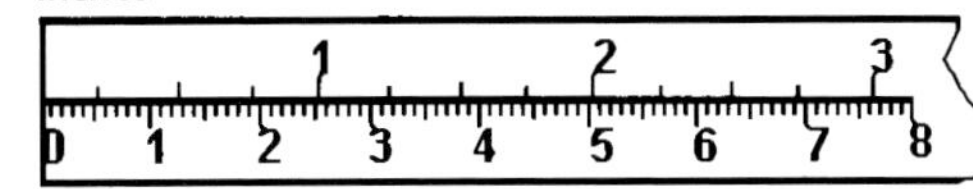

Japanese

記号

本書では、世界中の多くの言語に対応するため、文章による細かな説明をあえて避け、記号による解説を採用しました。そのため、魚種ごとの最も重要な特徴と飼育情報を簡単に得ることができます。飼育情報は原産地の自然環境下のものではなく、水槽飼育時におけるものです。

原産地（大陸別）
＊コードナンバーの前にあります。

A = アフリカ
E = ヨーロッパ
N = 北アメリカ
S = 中南米
X = アジアまたはオーストラリア

サイズ
＊コードの末尾にあります。

1 = 極小サイズ (稚魚/幼魚)
2 = 小サイズ (幼魚/販売可能サイズ)
3 = 中サイズ (未成魚/販売最適サイズ)
4 = 大サイズ (成魚/繁殖サイズ)
5 = 特大 サイズ(成魚)
6 = 超特大サイズ (展示用)

原産地
W = 天然物、ワイルド物
B = 養殖物、ブリード物
Z = 改良品種
X = 交雑種、ハイブリッド

大きさ
… cm = 成魚のおおよその体長

性別
♂（オス） ♀（メス） ♂♀(ペア)

水温
(通常の室温)
(大部分の熱帯魚の適温)
(ディスカスの適温)
(冷水魚/温帯魚)

pH-値（ペーハー値）
特別な水質調整は不要 (中性でよい)
やや低硬度の弱酸性を好む
高硬度のアルカリ性を好む

照明
○ 強い照明または日光を充分に
◑ 光は強すぎないように
◕ かなり暗めに

餌
☺ 雑食性で、乾燥飼料で特に構わない。
活餌や冷凍飼料など特別な飼料が必要
☹ 魚食性のため、生きた魚を与える
⦿ 藻食性のため、植物性の飼料が必要

遊泳層
中層から水槽全体
上層から水面付近
低層から水底

レイアウト
底砂+岩組み
岩組み+流木、または洞穴も
水草 +岩組+流木

生態/繁殖形態
ペアまたは3尾で飼育。
10尾以上の群れで飼育。
卵生
卵胎生または胎生
マウスブリーダー
ケイブブリーダー（穴の中にて産卵）
泡巣にて産卵
藻食性 /コケ取り (流木 +植物性飼料)
協調性が高く飼育は容易 (混泳水槽向け)
⚠ 飼育が難しいので、事前に専門書に目を通すこと
STOP 飼育はきわめて困難。経験豊かな上級者向け。
θ 生み出された卵には特別な処置が必要。
§ 保護対象種，特別許可が必要(CITES)
~L~ 両生的 (陸上部分が必要)
<Bw> 汽水性 (食塩を加えること)
~Sw~ 海産
<~Sw~ 幼魚期を海で過ごす (その後汽水域や淡水域へ移動)
~Sw~> 幼魚期を淡水域で過ごす (その後海へ移動)
<~Sw~> 海と淡水域を移動可能

必要な水槽のサイズ

SS	極小水槽	20-40 cm	5-20 l
S	小型水槽	40-80 cm	40-80 l
m	中型水槽	60-100 cm	80-200 l
L	大型水槽	100-200 cm	200-400 l
XL	超大型水槽	200-400 cm	400-3000 l
XXL	巨大水槽	over 400 cm	over 3000 l (特別展示用)

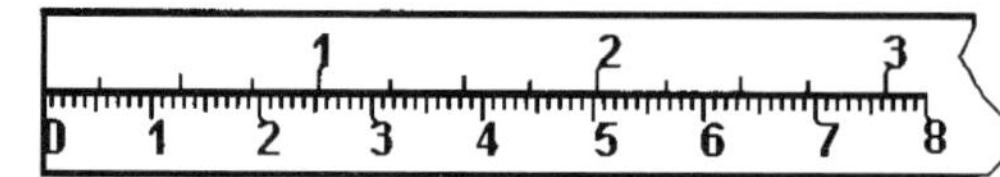

Simboli

Considerando la grande varietà di lingue in tutto il mondo, abbiamo deciso di internazionalizzare le dettagliate descrizioni dei testi, sostituendole con simboli internazionali.
Questi simboli sono sempre in relazione alle condizioni dell'acquario, non a quelli del paese d'origine o a biotipi.

Continente d'origine

verificare semplicemente la lettera di fronte al codice numerico

A = Africa
E = Europa
N = America del nord / usa
S = America del sud /latina
X = Asia + Australia

Eta'

l'ultimo numero del codice sta sempre per l'eta del pesce

1 = molto piccolo (avanotti/giovani)
2 = piccolo (giovane/taglia vendibile)
3 = medio (sub-adulto/ buona taglia da vendere)
4 = grande (adulto/ taglia da riproduzione)
5 = extra-grande(completamente adulto)
6 = eccezionalmente grande (specie da mostra)

Origine

W = di cattura
B = Allevati
Z = varietá coltivate e create per mano dell 'uomo
X = Forme ibride

Taglia

... cm = taglia che approsimativamente possono raggiungere da adulti

Sesso

♂ maschio  femmina  coppia

Temperatura

18–22°C (64–72°F) (temperatura ambiente)
22–25°C (72–77°F) (molti pesci tropicali)
24–29°C (75–85°F) (Discus etc.)
10–22°C (50–72°F) (freddo/temperato; America del nord/Europa)

pH-value

pH 6,5–7,2 nessuna richiesta particolare/neutra
pH 5,8–6,5 preferisce acqua leggermente acida e tenera
pH 7,5–8,5 preferisce acqua alcalina e dura

Illuminazione

○ illuminato/molta luce/ sole
◑ non molto illumninato
◕ molto scuro/ quasi buio

Alimentazione

☺ onnivori:cibo secco,non richieste particolari
diete speciali: mangime vivo o/e surgelato
☹ pescivori: si nutrono solamente di pesce vivo
erbivori; richiedono mangime vegetale

Posizione nell'acqua

a mezza acqua/tutti i livelli
livello superiore/abitante della superficie
livello inferiore/abitante del fondo

Decorazioni

solo rocce e substrato
rocce e legno, grotte
piante, rocce e legni

Comportamento/ riproduzione

si possono tenere in coppia o trio
pesci da branco, non tenerne meno di dieci
depositano strati di uova
vivipari
incubazione buccale
incubazione in cavità
incubazione tra bolle d'aria
magiatore di alga/pulitore vetro (legno di acquitrino+ mangime vegetale)
◇ pesce non aggressivo,facile da mantenere(acquario misto)
⚠ difficile da mantenere,leggere libri specilializzati
STOP attenzione,estremamente difficile ,consigliati solo per specialisti con esperienza
le uova neccessitano un trattamento speciale
§ specie protette, (WA), richiesta di permesso d'importazione (CITES)
~L~ anfibi(neccesitano di una porzione di terra)
<Bw> acqua salmastra (acqua +sale)
~Sw~ marini (vivono nel mare)
<~Sw~ in eta' giovanile vivono in acqua di mare ma poi possono viviere in acqua salmastra o dolce
~Sw~> in eta' giovanile in acqua dolce e piu' tardi in acqua di mare
<~Sw~>questi pesci vivono sia in acqua dolce che salata

dimensione degli acquari

SS	sueper-piccola	20–40 cm	5–20 l
S	piccola	40–80 cm	40–80 l
m	media	60–100 cm	80–200 l
L	grande	100–200 cm	200–400 l
XL	XL	200–400 cm	400–3 000 l
XXL	XXL	< 400 cm	< 3 000 l (acquario da vetrina)

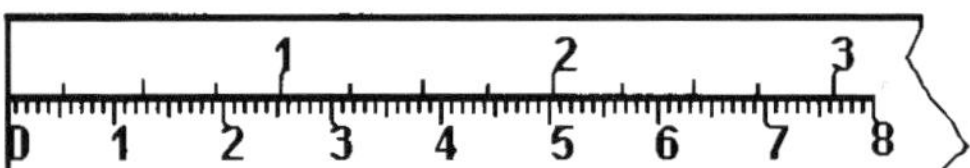

Symbols

Considering the great variety of languages worldwide, we have intentionally decided against detailed textual descriptions, replacing them by international symbols. This way, one can easily obtain the most important facts about the species and its care.
These care symbols always relate to the conditions in the aquarium, not the ones of the country of origin or biotopes.

continent of origin

simply check the letter in front of the code number

A = Africa **E** = Europe N = North America
S = Latin America **X** = Asia + Australia

age

the last figure of the code always stands for the age of the fish

1 = very small (fry/small juvenile)
2 = small (juvenile/saleable size)
3 = medium (sub-adult/good saleable size)
4 = large (adult/breeding size)
5 = extra large (fully-grown adult)
6 = exceptionally large (show specimen)

origin

W = wild-caught **B** = tank-bred
Z = cultivated form ("man-made" variety)
X = hybrid form

size

... cm = approximate size these fish can reach as adults

sex

♂ male ♀ female ♂♀ pair

temperature

18–22°C (64–72°F) (room temperature)
22–25°C (72–77°F) (many tropical fish)
24–29°C (75–85°F) (Discus etc.)
10–22°C (50–72°F) (cold/temperate; e.g. North America/Europe)

pH-value

pH 6,5–7,2 no special requirement (neutral)
pH 5,8–6,5 prefers soft, lightly acidic water
pH 7,5–8,5 prefers hard, alkaline water

lighting

bright, plenty of light / sun
not too bright
very dim

food

omnivorous: dry food, no special requirements
special diet: live food, frozen food
piscivore: feeds on (live) fish
herbivore: requires vegetable food

swimming level

mid-water/all levels
upper layer/surface dweller
lower level/bottom dweller

aquarium decor

just rocks and substrate
rocks and wood, caves
planted aquarium + rocks and wood

behaviour/reproduction

keep a pair or a trio
shoaling fish, do not keep less than 10
egglayer
livebearer/viviparous
mouthbrooder
cave brooder
bubblenest builder
algae eater /glass cleaner (bogwood + green food)
non-aggressive fish, easy to keep (mixed aquarium)
difficult to keep, read specialist literature beforehand
warning, extremely difficult, for experienced specialists only
the eggs need a special care
§ protected species, (WA), special license required ("CITES")
~L~ amphibic (needs land part)
<Bw> brackish water (water + additive salt)
~Sw~ marine (lives in the sea)
<~Sw~ juvenil in the sea (later as well in brackish water or fresh water)
~Sw~> juvenil in fresh water (later as well in the sea)
<~Sw~> as well in the sea and in fresh water (changes!)

minimum tank		length	capacity
ss	super-small	20–40 cm	5–20 l
s	small	40–80 cm	40–80 l
m	medium	60–100 cm	80–200 l
L	large	100–200 cm	200–400 l
XL	XL	200–400 cm	400–3 000 l
XXL	XXL	over 400 cm	over 3 000 l (display aquarium)

inches
1 2 3
0 1 2 3 4 5 6 7 8
centimetres

African Cichlids III
Malawi II

Kaiserbuntbarsche / Peacocks

Erwin Schraml

Die folgenden Bildautoren trugen zur inhaltlichen Gestaltung dieses Buches bei / *The following photographers and illustrators contributed to this volume:*

African Trading AB	Wilfried van der Elst
Ernst Klaban	Ad Konings
Steffen Lehner	Hans J. Mayland
Burkhard Migge	Schuzo Nakano
Marie-Paule Piednoir	Christian Piednoir
Peter Reinthal	A. J. Ribbink
Lothar Seegers	Mark Smith
Jos Snoeks	Andreas Spreinat
Wolfgang Staeck	Jochen Steves
Frank Teigler	George Turner
Christian Wyrwich	

Besonderer Dank geht auch an Aquarium Glaser, Rodgau, die uns in letzter Minute Bildmaterial der neuesten *Aulonocara*-Zuchtform „Dragon Blood" vermittelten.
Very special thanks to Aquarium Glaser, Rodgau, Germany, who obtained virtually in the last minute pictures of the latest *Aulonocara*, the „Dragon Blood".

AQUALOG: African Cichlids III
Malawi II
Kaiserbuntbarsche / Peacocks
Erwin Schraml
Rodgau: Aqualog-Verlag A.C.S. (AQUALOG)

NE: Schraml, E.

ISBN 3-936027-59-5

Fax: +49 (0) 6106 644 692
E-mail: info@aqualog.de
http://www.aqualog.de

Text und fachliche Bearbeitung
Erwin Schraml

Übersetzungen deutsch-englisch
Mary Bailey

Bildbearbeitung, Layout, Titelgestaltung
Verlag A.C.S.

Redaktion
Frank Schäfer

Druck, Satz, Verarbeitung:
Lithos: Verlag A.C.S.
Druck: Rohland & more, Offenbach
Gedruckt auf Magnostar glänzend,
100% chlorfrei von PWA umweltfreundlich
PRINTED IN GERMANY

Weitere nützliche Tips und Pflegehinweise finden Sie immer in der, alle sechs Wochen neu erscheinenden, ersten und einzigen internationalen Zeitschrift für Aquarianer ***AQUALOGnews***. Auch werden immer die neuesten Zuchtberichte darin veröffentlicht. Sie erscheint wahlweise in deutscher oder englischer Sprache. Sie erhalten die ***news*** im guten Zoofachhandel oder im Abonnement direkt vom Verlag. Fordern Sie ein kostenloses Probeexemplar an.

*Further useful tips about care and maintenance can be found every six weeks in **AQUALOGnews**, the unique journal for all friends of the hobby. Read, for example, the latest breeding reports in the **news**. It is available in German or English and can be obtained at your local pet shop or subscribed to at the publisher. Order your free specimen copy!*

Exclusive distributor of Aqualog Book Series in the USA:
Hollywood Import & Export, Inc.
PO BOX # 220024; Hollywood, FL 33022-0024; Tel: (954) 922 2970; Fax: (954) 926 5476; e-mail: aqualogusa@cs.com

Cover photos:

Front Cover:
Aulonocara jacobfreibergi „Orange"; A. kandeensis; photos: Andreas Spreinat; *A.* sp. „Stuartgranti Maleri"; photo: Burkhard Migge / Archiv A.C.S.

Back Cover:
Lethrinops sp. „Red Capuz"; photo: Erwin Schraml; *Aulonocara hansbaenschi* „Cape Maclear"; photo: Burkhard Migge / Archiv A.C.S.; *Tramitichromis intermedius; Astatotilapia calliptera;* photos: Erwin Schraml

Aulonocara und verwandte Gattungen

Aulonocara and related genera

Nach dem Mbuna-Band ist der Vorliegende nun der zweite Aqualog, der die Cichliden des Malawisees zum Thema hat. Lange Zeit haben Verlag und Autor darüber nachgedacht, ob es praktikabler ist einen einzigen Band, der alle sogenannte „Nicht-Mbunas" beinhaltet, zu produzieren oder das umfangreiche Thema weiter zu untergliedern. Aufgrund der Vielzahl an Arten und vor allem der gerade zur Zeit in vollem Gange befindlichen Forschungen sowie steter Neuentdeckungen, schien letzteres sinnvoller zu sein. Auch dieser Band sollte aber einer zusammenhängenden Gruppe gewidmet sein. Wir haben uns für die Kaiserbuntbarsche (*Aulonocara*) und die mit ihnen verwandten Arten entschieden.

Wie schon im ersten Malawi-Aqualog ist es gelungen, die bekanntesten Foto-Autoren zu überreden, ihre Archive für das Buch zu öffnen. Die Masse der Fotos stammt einmal mehr von Ad Konings und Andreas Spreinat, die beide als begnadete Unterwasserfotografen und Cichlidenfreaks in aller Welt bekannt sind. Ihnen beiden sei besonders herzlich gedankt, denn ohne ihre Vorarbeit wäre auch dieser Band nicht zustande gekommen. Auch wenn die anderen Bildautoren eine geringere Stückzahl von Fotos beigesteuert haben, wäre ohne ihr Zutun der Band nie vollständig geworden. So konnten Wissenschaftler und Aquarianer, wie Wilfried van der Elst, Ernst Klaban, Steffen Lehner, Hans J. Mayland, Burkhard Migge, Schuzo Nakano, Marie-Paule & Christian Piednoir, Peter Reinthal, A.J. (Tony) Ribbink, Lothar Seegers, Mark Smith, Jos Snoeks, Wolfgang Staeck, Jochen Steves, Frank Teigler, George Turner und Christian Wyrwich für Fotobeiträge gewonnen werden. Viel geholfen hat auch die Bereitwilligkeit von Großhändlern, ihre neuesten Importe fotografieren zu lassen. In diesem Zusammenhang möchte ich besonders dem leider inzwischen verstorbenen Marc Danhieux (Mal-Ta-Vi) danken. Die Belgische Cichlidenliefhebbers Vereniging hat durch ihre regelmäßig stattfindende Ausstellung in Antwerpen einen nicht unerheblichen Beitrag am Zustandekommen guter Fotodokumente geleistet. Auch Jos Snoeks (Afrikamuseum/Tervuren) möchte ich für seine Hilfen bei der Besprechung mancher systematischer und taxonomischer Probleme danken.

Die Malawisee-Cichliden spalten sich nach genetischen Untersuchungen in sechs verschiedene Verwandtschaftsgruppen auf, die schon als Aqualog behandelten Mbunas sind eine davon. Die anderen Gruppen sind jeweils die pelagisch lebenden Arten der Gattungen *Rhamphochromis* und *Diplotaxodon*, die einzelne Art *Astatotilapia calliptera*, verschiedene *Copadichromis*-Arten um *C. virginalis* (z.B. auch *C. ilesi*, nicht aber andere *Copadichromis*-Arten wie etwa *C. quadrimaculatus*, die eine weitere Gruppe stellen - die Gattung ist nach bisherigen Erkenntnissen also nicht monophyletisch) und, als sechste Gruppe, alle restlichen sogenannten „Nicht-Mbunas".

„*Alticorpus, Aulonocara* und *Lethrinops* sollten 'Mbuna', in einem phylogenetischen Sinn genannt werden", so hat Jos Snoeks (2000) in einer seiner Arbeiten geschrieben. Tatsächlich haben genetische Untersuchungen gezeigt, dass diese drei Gattungen näher mit den

Following the Mbuna volume, this is the second Aqualog to take the cichlids of Lake Malawi as its subject matter. Both publisher and author pondered for a long time whether it would be more practicable to produce a single volume containing all the so-called "non-mbuna" or to subdivide this extensive subject further. Because of the large number of species involved, and above all on account of the studies currently in progress as well as the constant new discoveries, in the final analysis the latter option appeared the more sensible. But we felt that even so this volume should be devoted to a discrete, coherent group. And we decided on the Malawi Peacocks (*Aulonocara*) and the species most closely related to them.

As in the case of first Malawi Aqualog, we have succeeded in persuading a number of renowned photographers to unlock their archives for this book. The bulk of the photos once again derive from Ad Konings and Andreas Spreinat, both known worldwide as talented underwater photographers and committed cichlid freaks. We are eternally grateful to them, as without their "groundwork" this volume could not have come into being. And although the other photographers involved have provided a smaller number of photos, this book would not have been complete without their contributions. So we would like to thank scientists and aquarists such as Wilfried van der Elst, Ernst Klaban, Steffen Lehner, Hans J. Mayland, Burkhard Migge, Schuzo Nakano, Marie-Paule & Christian Piednoir, Peter Reinthal, A.J. (Tony) Ribbink, Lothar Seegers, Mark Smith, Jos Snoeks, Wolfgang Staeck, Jochen Steves, Frank Teigler, George Turner and Christian Wyrwich for photographic contributions. The willingness of wholesalers to allow photographs to be taken of their latest imports has also been a great help, and in this respect I would particularly like to thank Marc Danhieux (Mal-Ta-Vi), who sadly has died in the meantime. The Belgian Cichlid Association has made a not inconsiderable contribution to the acquisition of top-quality photo-documentation via their regular exhibitions in Antwerp. And finally, I would like to thank Jos Snoeks (Africa Museum/Tervuren) for his help during discussions of a number of systematic and taxonomic problems.

On the basis of genetic studies the Lake Malawi cichlids can be divided into six different phylogenetic groups, one of which is the mbuna, already covered in a previous Aqualog. The other groups are the pelagic species of the genera *Rhamphochromis* and *Diplotaxodon*; the single species *Astatotilapia calliptera*; various *Copadichromis* species close to *C. virginalis* (for example *C. ilesi*); the remaining *Copadichromis* species such as, for example, *C. quadrimaculatus* (in other words, our current state of knowledge indicates that the genus *Copadichromis* is not monophyletic); and the sixth group which contains all the rest of the so-called "non-mbuna".

"*Alticorpus, Aulonocara* and *Lethrinops* should be termed 'Mbuna' in a phylogenetic sense", wrote Jos Snoeks (2000) in one of his works. And genetic studies have actually shown that these three genera are more closely related to the mbuna than

Mbunas verwandt sind, als mit irgendwelchen anderen Cichliden des Malawisees (HAUSER et al., 1999), obwohl sie bisher, rein morphologisch betrachtet, eigentlich als „Nicht-Mbunas" angesehen worden sind. Eine hübsche kleine Gruppe fanden wir, die gut in einem eigenen, diesem zweiten Malawi-Aqualog darzustellen ist, der damit praktisch auch an die schon behandelten Mbunas in verwandtschaftlicher Beziehung anknüpft. Da *Astatotilapia calliptera* eine Sonderstellung innerhalb der Malawisee-Cichliden einnimmt, wurde auch diese Art im vorliegenden Band berücksichtigt.

to any other cichlids from Lake Malawi (HAUSER *et al.*, 1999), although in the past, from a purely morphological viewpoint, they have in fact been regarded as "non-mbuna". An attractive small group, well suited to be presented in their own - this second - Malawi Aqualog, and following on neatly, phylogenetically speaking, from the mbuna already covered in the first volume. Because *Astatotilapia calliptera* occupies a special position among the Lake Malawi cichlids, this species too is discussed in the current volume.

Die Arten die früher einmal zu *Lethrinops* gezählt wurden, haben ECCLES & TREWAVAS (1989) in drei Gattungen aufgeteilt. Zusätzlich zu *Lethrinops* haben sie noch *Taeniolethrinops* und *Tramitichromis* geschaffen. Allerdings haben die schon erwähnten genetischen Untersuchungen gezeigt, dass alle *Taeniolethrinops* und die im flacheren Wasser lebenden *Lethrinops*-Arten, wie z.B. *Lethrinops albus, L. marginatus* und *L. auritus* nicht wie die in tieferen Bereichen lebenden *Lethrinops longipinnis, L. altus* und *L. gossei* (als Beispiele) zu den Mbunas näher verwandt sind, sondern mehr Erbsubstanz mit den „Nicht-Mbunas" teilen. Eine daraufhin unternommene Blitzuntersuchung von Jos SNOEKS (2001) hat ergeben, dass manche der Tiefwasser-*Lethrinops* gar keine typische *Lethrinops*-Bezahnung haben und damit in der Vergangenheit schlichtweg falsch eingruppiert worden sind. Dennoch sind alle Arten in diesem einen Band belassen worden, denn bisher haben sich die molekularen Untersuchungsergebnisse nicht in einer Änderung der Gattungszugehörigkeit niedergeschlagen. Genetische Untersuchungsergebnisse von Angehörigen der Gattung *Tramitichromis* hat Ben NGATUNGA in einer nicht veröffentlichten Doktorarbeit dargestellt, danach sind *Tramitichromis* ebenfalls näher mit den Flachwasser-*Lethrinops* und somit den „Nicht-Mbunas" verwandt.

The species that were formerly assigned to *Lethrinops* were divided into three genera by ECCLES & TREWAVAS (1989). In addition to *Lethrinops* they erected *Taeniolethrinops* and *Tramitichromis*. However, the genetic studies already mentioned have shown that all *Taeniolethrinops* and the *Lethrinops* species that live in shallower water (for example *Lethrinops albus, L. marginatus* and *L. auritus*) are not, unlike those that live in deeper water (for example, *Lethrinops longipinnis, L. altus* and *L. gossei*), closely related to the mbuna, but share more inherited traits with the "non-mbuna". A subsequent quick check undertaken by Jos SNOEKS (2001) has shown that some of the deep-water *Lethrinops* do not have typical *Lethrinops* dentition at all and have thus quite simply been incorrectly grouped with them in the past. All species have, nevertheless, been included in this volume, as to date the results of molecular studies have not precipitated any change in the generic placement. The results of genetic studies of members of the genus *Tramitichromis* have been presented by Ben NGATUNGA in an unpublished Ph.D. thesis, according to which *Tramitichromis* are again more closely related to the shallow-water *Lethrinops* and hence to the "non-mbuna".

Alticorpus STAUFFER & MCKAYE, 1988

Etymologie: Lat. ‚altus' - hoch; ‚corpus' - Körper; bezieht sich auf den Körperbau dieser Fische.
Typusart: *Alticorpus mentale* STAUFFER & MCKAYE, 1988.

Alticorpus STAUFFER & MCKAYE, 1988

Etymology: Latin *altus* = high + *corpus* = body, referring to the body form of these fishes.
Type species: *Alticorpus mentale* STAUFFER & MCKAYE, 1988.

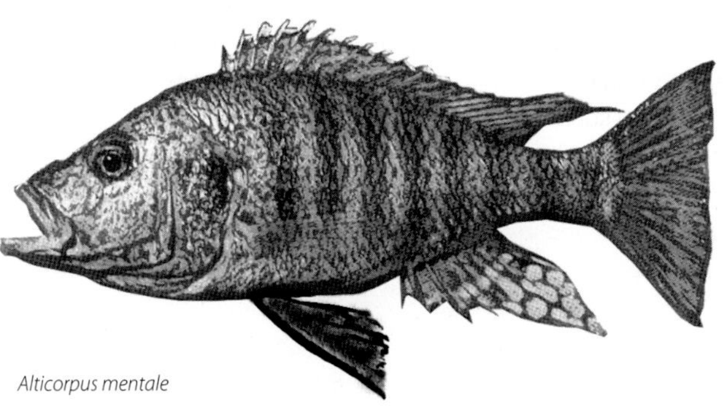

Alticorpus mentale

Dies ist eine im Malawisee endemische Gattung mit bisher relativ wenigen bekannten Arten. Keine davon ist bis heute als Aquarienfisch eingeführt worden. Das liegt daran, dass diese Cichliden überwiegend die Tiefen des Sees bewohnen (bis mind. 125 m, selten sind bisher Funde im Bereich von 20 m bekannt geworden). Zu den Merkmalen der Tiere gehören u.a. ein hochrückiger Körperbau, 6 bis 8 dunkle Querbalken auf den Seiten, ein vorstehender Unterkiefer und zahlreiche Sinnesporen im Kopfbereich. Neuere Untersuchungen und das Auffinden weiterer neuer Arten mit Sinnesporen am Kopf (SNOEKS & WALAPA, 1999) machen es derzeit schwierig, die Gattung *Alticorpus* überhaupt von *Aulonocara* zu unterscheiden.

This is a genus endemic to Lake Malawi, with relatively few species known to date. So far none of them have been imported as aquarium fishes. This is because these cichlids live predominantly in the depths of the lake (down to at least 125 m; to date only rare finds are known from the 20 m zone). The characters of these fishes include, *inter alia*, a high-backed body shape, 6 to 8 dark vertical bars on the flanks, a projecting lower jaw, and numerous sensory pores in the head region. Recent studies and the discovery of additional new species with sensory pores on the head (SNOEKS & WALAPA, 1999) mean that it is at present difficult to differentiate the genus *Alticorpus* from *Aulonocara*.

KONINGS (1990) machte darauf aufmerksam, dass *Alticorpus pectinatum* vielleicht ein Synonym zu *A. peterdaviesi* sein könnte. TURNER

KONINGS (1990) pointed out that *Alticorpus pectinatum* may perhaps be a synonym of *A. peterdaviesi*. TURNER (1996) summarises

(1996) fasst die entsprechenden Argumente zusammen: *A. peterdaviesi* wurde anhand von zwei Exemplaren beschrieben, der Holotypus wurde im US National Museum hinterlegt, der Paratypus im Britischen Museum (nach SNOEKS & WALAPA (in SNOEKS 2004) sind beide im USNM hinterlegt). Eine Untersuchung des Paratypus durch TREWAVAS (pers. comm. an TURNER) ergab, dass er der Beschreibung von *A. pectinatum* entspricht. STAUFFER (pers. comm. an TURNER) untersuchte den Holotypus und befand ihn als verschieden von *A. pectinatum*. Zwar hatte keiner dieser beiden Autoren den jeweils anderen Typus untersucht, aber TURNER kommt aufgrund der Aussagen zu dem Schluss, dass beide Arten valide sind und nur der Paratypus von *A. peterdaviesi* nun als zu *A. pectinatum* zugehörig betrachtet werden muss.

Diese Ansicht teilen SNOEKS & WALAPA (in SNOEKS, 2004) nicht. Die Gründe für die Unterschiede, die bei TURNER wiedergegeben sind, resultieren ihrer Ansicht nach daraus, dass z.B. für Farbmerkmale ein Bild in KONINGS (1990) hergenommen wurde, das nicht, wie angenommen, den Holotypus sondern den Paratypus zeigt. Unterschiede in meristischen Werten zwischen den beiden Arten verschwanden, als sie die Daten von STAUFFER & MCKAYE (1988) mit 20 weiteren Exemplaren verglichen, die zuvor als *A. pectinatum* aufgeschlüsselt worden sind. Aufgrund von Literaturangaben und eigenen Untersuchungen konnten sie deshalb nur zu der Anschauung gelangen, dass *A. pectinatum* wahrscheinlich doch ein Synonym zu *A. peterdaviesi* ist.

Außerdem stellen SNOEKS & WALAPA (in SNOEKS, 2004) fünf weitere *Alticorpus*-Arten vor, die sie allerdings noch nicht formell beschreiben. Zwar passen sie insgesamt am ehesten zum Erscheinungsbild von *Alticorpus*, dennoch bleiben den Autoren Zweifel, da diese Arten z.B. in der äußeren Zahnreihe zweispitzige Zähne haben und außerdem allesamt offenbar eine geringere Endgröße erreichen als typische *Alticorpus*-Arten. Sie scheinen auf bestimmte Weise eine Brücke zwischen dieser Gattung und *Aulonocara* zu schaffen und lassen vermuten, dass der morphologische Unterschied der beiden Gattungen nicht so groß ist wie gedacht.

Da Fische aus größerer Wassertiefe nur sehr langsam und durch ständigen Druckausgleich an die Oberfläche gebracht werden können, ohne ihren Tod herbeizuführen, ist es fraglich, wann wir *Alticorpus*-Arten einmal im Aquarium pflegen können. Unmöglich ist es nicht, wie wir am Beispiel von manchen Cichliden aus dem Tanganjikasee mit ähnlichen Habitatsvorlieben gesehen haben.

Astatotilapia PELLEGRIN, 1904

Etymologie: gr. ‚astatos', unstet (bezieht sich wahrscheinlich auf die Variabilität innerhalb der Gattung) + tilapia, dem Namen einer anderen Buntbarschgattung;
Typusart: *Sparus desfontainii* LACEPÈDE, 1802.

Die Gattung ist derzeit nach rein morphologischen Kriterien definiert und soll ein extrem weites Verbreitungsgebiet besitzen, das vom Nahen Osten (also noch auf dem asiatischen Kontinent), dem Norden Afrikas (hier kommt die Typusart *A. desfontainii* her), im Tschad-Becken, entlang des Nils, im afrikanischen Grabenbruch, über Ostafrika bis zum nordöstlichen Süden Afrikas reicht. Nach

the relevant arguments: *A. peterdaviesi* was described from two specimens, with the holotype deposited in the US National Museum and the paratype in the Natural HistoryMuseum in London (according to SNOEKS & WALAPA (in SNOEKS 2004) both are deposited in USNM). An investigation of the paratype by TREWAVAS (pers. comm. to TURNER) showed that it matches the description of *A. pectinatum*. STAUFFER (pers. comm. to TURNER) examined the holotype and found it different to A. *pectinatum*. Admittedly neither of these two authors examined the other type specimen, but on the basis of their findings TURNER came to the conclusion that both species are valid and that henceforth only the paratype of *A. peterdaviesi* should be regarded as belonging to *A. pectinatum*

This view is not shared by SNOEKS & WALAPA (in SNOEKS 2004). In their view the reasons for the differences cited by TURNER may derive from the fact that his colour characteristics, for example, were taken from a photo in KONINGS (1990) which showed not the holotype as assumed but the paratype. Differences in meristic values between the two species disappeared when they compared the data of STAUFFER & MCKAYE (1988) with 20 additional specimens that had previously been keyed out as *A. pectinatum*. On the basis of data in the literature and their own researches they could thus only conclude that *A. pectinatum* is probably a synonym of *A. peterdaviesi*.

In addition, SNOEKS & WALAPA (in SNOEKS 2004) recognise five additional *Alticorpus* species, which they do not, however, formally describe. Although these species generally accord better with the phenotype of *Alticorpus*, the authors nevertheless remain in some doubt, because, for example, these species have bicuspid teeth in the outer series, and, moreover, all apparently attain a smaller eventual size than typical *Alticorpus* species. In some ways they appear to constitute a bridge between this genus and Aulonocara, leading to the supposition that the morphological distinctions between the two genera may not be as great as hitherto thought.

Because fishes from great depths can be brought to the surface alive only very slowly and with gradual decompression, it is questionable if and when we will be able to maintain *Alticorpus* species in the aquarium. But it is not impossible, as we have seen in the case of a number of cichlids from Lake Tanganyika with similar habitat preferences.

Astatotilapia PELLEGRIN, 1904

Etymology: Greek *astatos* = unstable, (perhaps referring to variability within the genus, the difficulty of defining it clearly) + *Tilapia*, the name of another genus of cichlids;
Type species: *Sparus desfontainii* LACEPÈDE, 1802.

The genus is at present defined purely on morphological criteria and has an extremely broad distribution extending from the Near East (in other words part of the continent of Asia) across the north of Africa (from which comes the type species, *A. desfontainii*) to the Tschad basin, along the Nile, through the African Rift Valley, and across East Africa to the north-eastern

einer Bearbeitung von VAN OIJEN (1996) zählen keine der lacustrinen Arten aus dem Victoriasee-Becken zur Gattung. Die Zugehörigkeit vieler anderer Arten ist fraglich. Bei neueren Untersuchungen wurden die von GREENWOOD vormals gefundenen Unterschiede von *Astatotilapia* zu den Gattungen *Yssichromis, Paralabidochromis* und *Gaurochromis* nicht bestätigt, bzw. durch neu gefundene Arten überbrückt. Aufgrund der ungeklärten Zuordnung von Arten sind echte *Astatotilapia* z.Zt. nur von Oasen Nordafrikas und in Fließgewässern Ostafrikas bekannt, wo sie evtl. auch in einzelnen Seen vorkommen.

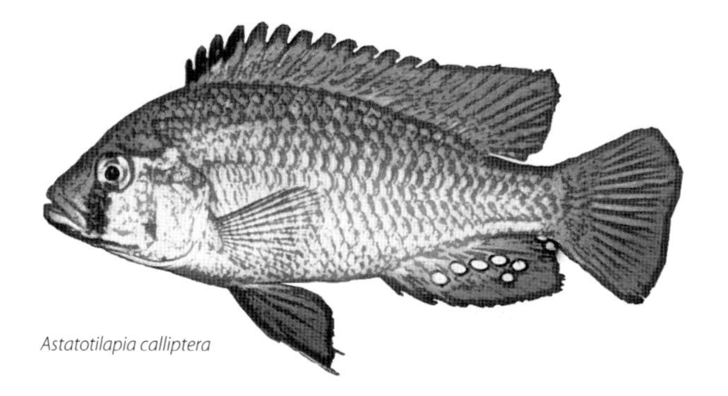

Astatotilapia calliptera

part of southern Africa. Following a revision by VAN OIJEN (1996) none of the lacustrine species from the Lake Victoria basin are now regarded as belonging to the genus. The inclusion of many other species is questionable. More recent studies do not confirm the differences previously discovered by GREENWOOD between *Astatotilapia* and the genera *Yssichromis, Paralabidochromis* and *Gaurochromis*, which are "bridged" by newly discovered species. Because of the unclear generic placement of the species, at present true *Astatotilapia* are known only from oases in North Africa and the rivers of East Africa, where they also in fact occur in individual lakes as well.

Nur eine Art aus dem Malawisee wurde und wird auch noch gegenwärtig der Gattung *Astatotilapia* zugeordnet: *A. calliptera*. Ursprünglich als *Chromis callipterus* von GÜNTHER (1894) mit Typusfundort 'Malawisee' beschrieben und später in *Haplochromis* geführt, galt sie lange Zeit als vermeintlicher Vorläufer und Urvater der Malawisee-Haplochrominen. Dafür sprach z.B. auch, dass sie nicht nur im Malawisee selbst, sondern auch in den umliegenden Flüssen zu finden ist. LIPPITSCH (1993) konnte aber zeigen, dass die Beschuppung dieser Art viel ähnlicher zu denen des Victoriasee-Superflocks ist als zu anderen Malawisee Cichliden. Eine neuere Untersuchung von SEEHAUSEN et al. (2002) mit „nuclear markers" ergab nun aber wiederum, dass die *A. calliptera*, die im Malawisee gefunden werden, sehr viel mehr genetische Übereinstimmungen mit anderen Arten aus dem Malawisee haben (besonders mit *Diplotaxodon limnothrissa* z.B., aber eben auch mit vielen anderen Arten aus unterschiedlichen Gattungen, wie *Taeniolethrinops* oder diversen Mbunas) als mit den bisher ebenfalls zur Art *Astatotilapia calliptera* gerechneten Populationen aus den umliegenden Gewässern (untersucht wurde eine Population aus dem Zambesi River).

Only one species comes from Lake Malawi and this too is still currently assigned to the genus *Astatotilapia*: *A. calliptera*, originally described as *Chromis callipterus* by GÜNTHER (1894) with the type locality Lake Malawi, and subsequently transferred to *Haplochromis*, has long been regarded as the presumptive precursor and primeval ancestor of the Lake Malawi haplochromines. This is also supported by, for example, the fact that it is found not only in Lake Malawi itself, but also in the surrounding rivers. LIPPITSCH (1993), however, has been able to demonstrate that the scalation of this species is more similar to that of the Lake Victoria super-flock than that of other Lake Malawi cichlids. Then again, a more recent study by SEEHAUSEN *et al.* (2002) using "nuclear markers" indicates that the *A. calliptera* found in Lake Malawi have a far greater genetic correlation with other species from Lake Malawi (in particular with *Diplotaxodon limnothrissa*, for example, but also with numerous other species from various genera such as *Taeniolethrinops* and assorted mbuna) than with populations from surrounding waters (a population from the Zambezi River was studied) to date likewise assigned to the species *Astatotilapia calliptera*.

Inwiefern *A. calliptera* mit anderen ähnlich Arten auch heute noch verwechselt wird, ist spekulativ. Tatsache ist, dass behauptet wird, dass sie zusammen mit *A. tweddlei* in den Lakes Chilwa and Chiuta vorkommen soll. Das enorm weite Verbreitungsgebiet umfasst zusätzlich noch das Rovuma River System, den Ruo River im südlichen Malawi, sowie stromabwärts vom Austritt des Malawisees in den Shire River und Lake Malombe, das untere Zambesi System, außerdem noch weitere Flüsse in Mozambique die in den Indischen Ozean entwässern, wie etwa der Pungwe, Buzi und untere Save River. Es erscheint fragwürdig, dass alles dies nur eine Art sein soll, und dass diese Fische *Astatotilapia* sind, ist eigentlich bereits widerlegt. Warten wir also wieder auf einen neuen Namen für den Callipterus.

We can only speculate on the extent to which *A. calliptera* is still confused with other similar species. It is a fact that it has been asserted that it occurs together with *A. tweddlei* in Lakes Chilwa and Chiuta. Its enormously wide distribution region also includes the Rovuma River system, the Ruo River in the south of Malawi, as well as upstream to the outlet of Lake Malawi into the Shire River and Lake Malombe, the lower Zambezi System, plus other rivers in Mozambique that drain into the Indian Ocean, for example the Pungwe, the Buzi, and the lower Save River. It seems questionable whether all all these can be a single species, and it has already in fact been questioned whether these fishes belong to *Astatotilapia*. So we must expect a new name for the Callipterus.

Aulonocara REGAN, 1922

Etymologie: Gr. ‚aulos' - Leitung + ‚kara' - Kopf; auf die stark entwickelten sensorischen Kanäle im Kopfbereich verweisend.
Typusart: *Aulonocara nyassae* REGAN, 1922.

Aulonocara REGAN, 1922

Etymology: Greek . *aulos* = pipe + *kara* = head; referring to the inflated cephalic sensory canals.
Type species: *Aulonocara nyassae* REGAN, 1922.

Die Gattung *Aulonocara* besteht aus zwei, unterschiedliche Lebensräume bewohnenden, Gruppen. Zum einen die psammophilen Arten, die über Sandgrund leben, und zum anderen die lithophilen, die im Bereich von Felsen anzutreffen sind. Allen Arten ist gemeinsam, dass sie über stark vergrößerte Sinnesgruben im Kopfbereich verfügen, besonders gut an der Unterseite des Unterkiefers zu sehen. Dieses Merkmal teilen sie unter allen Malawicichliden nur mit *Alticorpus*.

The genus *Aulonocara* consists of two groups that inhabit different habitats, on the one hand the psammophilous species that live over sandy bottoms, and on the other the lithophilous species that are found in the vicinity of rocks. All species share the common feature of greatly enlarged sensory pits in the head region, particularly visible on the underside of the lower jaw. Among the Malawi cichlids they share this character only with *Alticorpus*.

Die Angehörigen der Gattung *Aulonocara* haben den Wissenschaftlern die an ihnen arbeiteten, seit Anbeginn große Schwierigkeiten hinsichtlich einer korrekten Identifikation gemacht. ECCLES (in ECCLES & TREWAVAS, 1989) hat bei der wirklich kleinen Typenserie (nur drei Individuen) der Typusart feststellen müssen, dass sie aus zwei verschiedenen Arten besteht. *Aulonocara nyassae* basiert derzeit deshalb nur auf dem Holotypus, der ein Weibchen ist. Die beiden Syntypen wurden als neue Art (*A. guentheri*) beschrieben. Der Name *A. nyassae* wurde in der aquaristischen Literatur sehr populär, weil die ersten Kaiserbuntbarsch-Arten, die im Handel erhältlich waren, so bezeichnet wurden. Später (1984) erkannte TREWAVAS, dass diese Fische wissenschaftlich noch unbekannt waren und MEYER et al. beschrieben sie 1987 als *A. hansbaenschi* zusammen mit fünf weiteren Arten. Schon kurz darauf bemängelte STAECK (1988) die Qualität und den Nutzen mancher dieser Diagnosen. Leider übernahmen ECCLES & TREWAVAS in ihrer umfassenden Malawi-Haplochrominen-Revision die Bezeichnungen von MEYER et al. kritiklos.

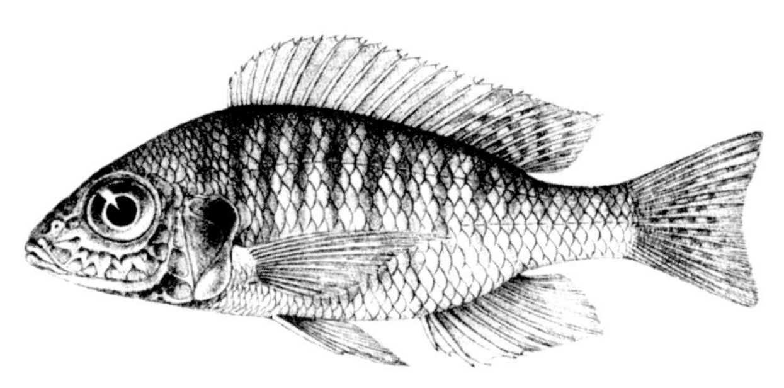

Aulonocara nyassae — after: ECCLES & TREWAVAS, 1989

Right from the start the members of the genus *Aulonocara* have caused great difficulties - as regards correct identification - for the scientists working on them. ECCLES (in ECCLES & TREWAVAS, 1989) established that the very small type series (only three individuals) of the type species consisted of two different species. As a result since then *Aulonocara nyassae* has been based on the holotype alone, which is a female. The two syntypes were described as a new species (*A. guentheri*). The name *A. nyassae* became very commonplace in the aquarium literature, as the first Malawi Peacock species available in the trade were labelled thus. Later (1984) TREWAVAS realised that these fishes were unknown to science and MEYER *et al.* described them in 1987 as *A. hansbaenschi*, along with five additional species. Not long afterwards STAECK (1988) criticised the quality and the usage of some of these diagnoses. Unfortunately in their comprehensive revision of the Malawi haplochromines ECCLES & TREWAVAS adopted the designations of MEYER *et al.*without any critical review.

Nach den Veröffentlichungen von MEYER et al. wurden in der Aquaristik zunächst alle ganz oder überwiegend blau gefärbten Arten, mit mehr oder weniger großen Partien von rotbrauner bis roter Farbe aus dem südöstlichen Teil des Malawisees, *A. hansbaenschi* (Typuslokalität südlich von Masinje) zugeschrieben. Ebenfalls ganz oder überwiegend blau gefärbte Arten mit gelb bis orange gefärbten Partien aus dem nordwestlichen Teil hingegen *A. stuartgranti* (Typuslokalität Chilumba/Mpanga Rocks). Dazwischen gibt es mit *A. baenschi* eine überwiegend gelb gefärbte Art vom Nkhomo Reef bei Benga. Auch die weit südlich von Benga bei den Maleri-Inseln und in deren Nachbarschaft bei den Chidunga Rocks bekannt gewordenen gelblichen bzw. orangen Formen wurden zunächst *A. baenschi* zugeordnet. Desgleichen die weit nördlich von Benga bei Usisya vorkommenden gelblichen Tiere mit blauem Kopf. Eine nur schwer von der Usisya-Population zu unterscheidende Art von Kande (diese Insel liegt deutlich näher zu Usisya als zu Benga und außerdem dazwischen), wurde hingegen als A. steveni beschrieben. Die am Ostufer gegenüber von Usisya und Kande vorkommenden Fische mit ähnlicher Färbung aber rundlicherem Kopf, wurden von Aquarianern ebenfalls *A. steveni* zugeordnet.

Following the publication of the descriptions of MEYER *et al*, all completely or predominantly blue-coloured species with more or less large areas of red-brown to red colour, from the south-eastern part of Lake Malawi, were initially ascribed to *A. hansbaenschi* (type locality south .of Masinje) in the aquarium hobby. On the other hand, a completely or predominantly blue-coloured species with yellow to orange areas, from the north-western part, was identified as *A. stuartgranti* (type locality Chilumba/Mpanga Rocks). In between there was *A. baenschi*, a predominantly yellow-coloured species from Nkhomo Reef near Benga. The yellowish and/or orange forms known from the Maleri Islands and nearby at Chidunga Rocks, far to the south of Benga, were also initially assigned to *A. baenschi*. Likewise the yellowish fishes with blue heads from Usisya, far to the north of Benga. On the other hand, a species from Kande (this island lies between Usisya and Benga, and significantly closer to the former), distinguishable only with difficulty from the Usisya population, was described as *A. steveni*. The fishes with similar coloration but a more rounded head, from the eastern shore opposite Usisya and Kande, were likewise assigned to *A. steveni* by aquarists.

KONINGS (1995) zog seine Konsequenzen aus nicht wirklich vorhandenen oder unglücklich gezogenen Abgrenzungen der Arten und betrachtet *A. hansbaenschi* und *A. steveni* als Synonym zum etwas

KONINGS (1995), basing his conclusions on the in fact non-existent or poorly defined distinctions between the species, regarded *A. hansbaenschi* and *A. steveni* as synonyms of *A. stuartgranti*, which

früher beschriebenen *A. stuartgranti*. Allerdings gesteht er den Populationen von Maleri und Mbenji einen eigenen, noch nicht durch einen wissenschaftlichen Namen manifestierten Artstatus zu. Nicht so konsequent ist sein Vorgehen bei den Arten, die er dem „Chitande Type"-Komplex (auch „Chitendi"-Komplex genannt) zuordnet. Hier bezeichnet er viele Formen so, als wären es eigenständige Arten, obwohl RIBBINK et al. (1983) viele dieser Fische einer Art zuweisen, die sie als Aulonocara „Blue Collar" bezeichnen. Die Bezeichnung „Chitendi-Type" stammt von der Insel Chitande (auch Chitendi genannt) bei Chilumba. Dort wurde eine Art gefangen, die später als *A. ethelwynnae* beschrieben wurde. Ähnliche Formen von ganz anderen Gegenden des Sees erhielten den Zusatz „Chitendi/ Chitande-Type". Diese Formen ähneln sich in der Art und Weise wie es die „Stuartgrantis" tun.

Insgesamt ist die gegenwärtige Situation bezüglich der Identifizierbarkeit vieler *Aulonocara*-Arten sehr unbefriedigend. Ob es tatsächlich Arten gibt, die eine seeweite Verbreitung besitzen und nur je nach Fundort unterschiedlich aussehen, oder ob es nicht doch sogar mehr Arten in den betreffenden Gruppen gibt, als gegenwärtig beschrieben sind, ist noch ungewiss. Auch durch die immer noch neuen Formen von Kaiserbuntbarschen, die gefunden werden, wird sich in dieser Gattung künftig taxonomisch sicherlich noch einiges tun.

Lethrinops REGAN, 1922

Etymologie: Hergeleitet von der marinen Fischgattung *Lethrinus* + Gr. ‚opsis' - Aussehen; auf die äußere Ähnlichkeit mit dieser Gattung verweisend.
Typusart: *Chromis lethrinus* GÜNTHER, 1893.

Unter modernen Wissenschaftlern (z.B. SNOEKS, 2000) gilt gerade *Lethrinops* als typisches Beispiel für das kümmerliche Wissen, das wir von vielen Malawisee-Cichliden besitzen. TURNER (1996) fasst die unzulängliche Art und Weise, wie in der Vergangenheit mit *Lethrinops*-Arten im wissenschaftlichen Sinn umgegangen wurde, zusammen. ECCLES & LEWIS z.B. haben in mehreren Arbeiten in den späten 1970ern einige der alten Arten wieder- oder andere neu beschrieben. Allerdings basierten einige der Wiederbeschreibungen auf Material das nicht artgleich mit dem Typenmaterial war, welches teilweise gar nicht untersucht und vermessen wurde. Außerdem sind manche ihrer Belegexemplare schon verloren gegangen, bevor ihre Arbeit darüber veröffentlicht war und andere, die in der Feldkollektion auf Monkey Bay deponiert waren, sind sogar lange zuvor zerstört gewesen. Derzeit kann deshalb das Wissen über diese große und für die Proteingewinnung kommerziell wichtige Gruppe nur als bruchstückhaft beschrieben werden. Dies gilt auch im aquaristischen Sinne, denn bisher sind von sehr wenigen der etwa 50 bekannten *Lethrinops*-Arten Zuchtberichte veröffentlicht worden (damit sind alle nominellen Arten plus die bisher nur mit Arbeitsbezeichnungen, Cheironymen, belegten Formen gemeint).

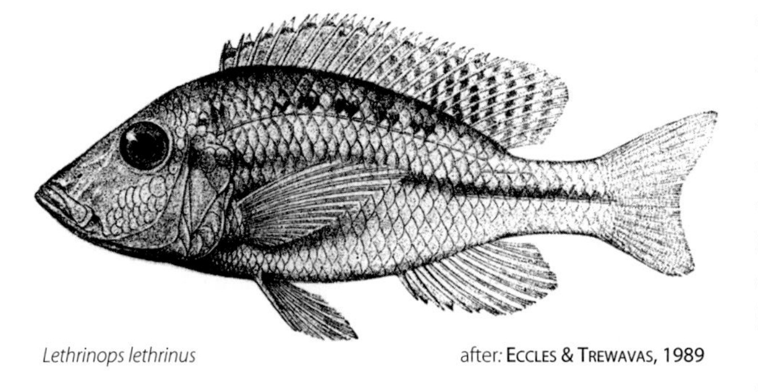

Lethrinops lethrinus — after: ECCLES & TREWAVAS, 1989

was described slightly earlier. However, he considered the populations from Maleri and Mbenji to deserve the status of a separate species, not yet distinguished by a scientific name. He is less than consistent in his view of the species which he assigns to the "Chitande Type" complex (also known as the "Chitendi" complex). Here he treats numerous forms as if they were distinct species, although Ribbink *et al.* (1983) ascribe many of these fishes to a single species which they term *Aulonocara* "Blue Collar". The designation "Chitande Type" derives from the island of Chitande (also called Chitendi) near Chilumba, where a species was collected that was subsequently described as *A. ethelwynnae*. Similar forms from completely different areas of the lake received the label "Chitande Type" or "Chitendi Type". These forms resemble one another in much the same way as the various "Stuartgrantis".

All in all, the current situation regarding the identity of many *Aulonocara* species is very unsatisfactory. It remains unclear whether there really are species with a lake-wide distribution which simply look different depending on the locality, or whether there are are even more species in the relevant groups than have so far been described. In addition, the continually increasing number of new forms of Malawi Peacocks being discovered will undoubtedly have an impact on the future taxonomy of the genus.

Lethrinops REGAN, 1922

Etymology: Derived from the marine fish genus *Lethrinus* + Greek *opsis* = appearance; referring to the external similarity to that genus.
Type species: *Chromis lethrinus* GÜNTHER, 1893.

Among modern scientists (for example SNOEKS, 2000), *Lethrinops* is regarded as a typical example of the pitiful state of our knowledge of many Lake Malawi cichlids. TURNER (1996) summarises the inadequate manner in which *Lethrinops* species have been treated (in a scientific sense) in the past. For example, in the late 1970s ECCLES & LEWIS redescribed a number of the existing species and described others as new. However, some of their redescriptions were based on material that was not conspecific with the type material, which in some cases wasn't examined or measured at all. In addition, some of their specimens had already been lost before their work on them was published, and others, deposited in the field collection at Monkey Bay, had even been destroyed long before. Hence at the present time our knowledge of this large group, commercially important as a source of protein, can at best be described as fragmentary. This also applies in the aquarium hobby, as to date breeding reports have been published on only a very few of the approximately 50 known *Lethrinops* species (by which is meant all the nominal species plus those forms so far given only "working names").

Nach der Revision durch ECCLES & TREWAVAS sind in *Lethrinops* nur Arten enthalten, die sich aufgrund der Bezahnung ähnlich sind. Im Unterkiefer können zwei bis fünf Reihen von Zähnen stehen, in der äußeren Reihe sind sie vorne zwei- und dreispitzig, hinten aber nur einspitzig. Die Anordnung der Zähne auf dem Unterkiefer ist besonders charakteristisch (s. Abb.). Die äußere Zahnreihe ist hinten einwärts gekrümmt. Die inneren Zahnreihen enden nur kurz vor dem Ende der äußeren.

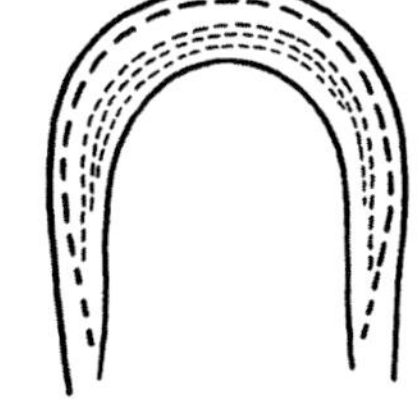

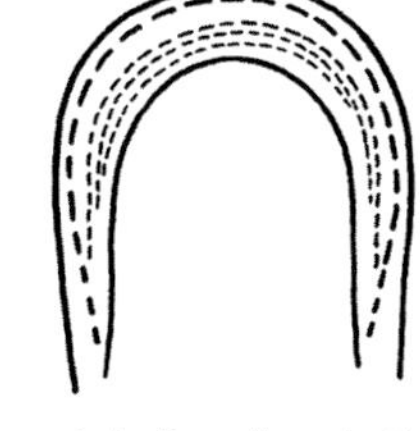

Schematische Darstellung der Zahnreihen im Unterkiefer eines *Haplochromis*-artigen (links) und eines *Lethrinops*-artigen (rechts).
Schematic presentation of the dental arcardes in the lower jaw in a *Haplochromis*-type (left) and a *Lethrinops*-type (right).

After SNOEKS, 2004

Bei der systematischen Einteilung vieler Malawisee-Cichliden kommt aber auch dem Farbmuster, und zwar dem Melaninfarbmuster, eine wichtige Rolle zu. Das sind die schwarzen Farbelemente, die auch bei konservierten Tieren gut zu erkennen sind. Bei *Lethrinops* entspricht das Melaninmuster entweder dem sogenannten primitiven Typ (vertikale Barren auf den Flanken und/oder ein horizontaler Mittelstreifen) oder zeigt unterschiedliche Stufen der Reduktion der horizontalen Elemente zu Flecken. Bei den meisten Arten sind überhaupt nur die vertikalen Zeichnungselemente ausgebildet. Viele nominelle Arten sind sich sehr ähnlich oder könnten daher Synonyme sein. Einige Arten variieren standortabhängig in der Färbung. Es gibt *Lethrinops*-Arten, die im Tiefwasser leben und solche, die im Flachwasser vorkommen. Innerhalb der Gattung lassen sich zwei Gruppen unterscheiden: Arten, die über Sandboden leben, haben eine zugespitzte Kopfform, kauen den Sand durch und fressen im Boden lebende Insektenlarven und Mollusken. Sie stellen einen wichtigen Bestandteil des für die Proteingewinnung kommerziell wichtigen Fischfangs dar. Arten, die in der Fels- und Übergangszone leben, sind kurzköpfig und haben eine besonders kräftige Schlundknochenbezahnung, was darauf hindeutet, dass sie von Mollusken leben. Diese Gruppe ist aufgrund der attraktiven Färbung der Männchen aquaristisch interessanter. Bisher wurden nur wenige *Lethrinops*-Arten als Aquarienfische eingeführt.

Aufgrund neuerer molekularer Untersuchungen (HAUSER et al., 1999) scheinen die Tiefwasser-Formen von *Lethrinops* zusammen mit einigen anderen Gruppen, in eine phylogenetische Linie zu gehören, die sich klar von den Flachwasser bewohnenden Arten unterscheidet. Diese Beobachtung lässt Zweifel über den Nutzen der Bezahnung als Unterscheidungsmerkmal der Gattung aufkommen. Auf der anderen Seite haben kurze Überprüfungen der Bezahnung dieser Tiefwasser-Formen, die durch andere Wissenschaftler vorgenommen wurden (SNOEKS, 2001) ergeben, dass die Fische überhaupt nicht die Bezahnung haben, die für *Lethrinops* typisch ist und deshalb in der Vergangenheit zu unrecht in die Gattung eingeordnet waren.

Taeniolethrinops ECCLES & TREWAVAS, 1989

Etymologie: Gr. ‚tainia' - Streifen + lethrinops (siehe oben); verweist auf das für die Diagnose der Gattung wichtige Streifenmuster.
Typusart: *Haplochromis praeorbitalis* REGAN, 1922.

Aufgrund eines besonderen Zeichnungsmerkmals, nämlich des

Following the revision by ECCLES & TREWAVAS, *Lethrinops* now includes only species that are similar on the basis of their dentition. The teeth in the lower jaw are in two to five series; those of the outer series are bicuspid or tricuspid anteriorly and unicuspid posteriorly; and the outer series curves inwards posteriorly, ending just behind the inner series.

However, the colour pattern, specifically the melanin pattern, also plays an important role in the systematic placement of many Lake Malawi cichlids. The melanin pattern consists of the black elements in the coloration, which are also readily apparent in preserved specimens. In *Lethrinops* the melanin pattern either corresponds to the so-called primitive type (vertical bars on the flanks and/or a horizontal mid-lateral band) or shows varying degrees of reduction of the horizontal components to form blotches. In most species only the vertical pattern elements are developed. On this basis many of the nominal species are very similar to one another or may be synonymous. A number of species vary in their coloration depending on the locality. There are *Lethrinops* species that live in deep water and others that occur in shallow water. Two groups can be distinguished within the genus. Firstly, species that live over sandy bottoms, have a pointed head shape, and sift through the sand, feeding on insect larvae and molluscs living in the substrate; these species represent a significant component of the commercial fishery, important as a source of protein. Secondly, species that live in the rocky and intermediate zones, have short heads, and possess a particularly powerful pharyngeal dentition, indicating that they feed on molluscs. Because of the attractive coloration of the males, this group is of greater aquarium-hobby interest. To date only a few *Lethrinops* species have been imported as aquarium fishes.

On the basis of recent molecular studies (HAUSER *et al.*, 1999) it appears that the deep-water forms of *Lethrinops*, together with a number of other groups, belong in a single phylogenetic clade (branch) which is clearly distinct from that containing the shallow-water species. This finding casts doubt upon the validity of the dentition as a diagnostic character of the genus. On the other hand, quick checks of the dentition of the deep-water forms undertaken by other scientists (SNOEKS, 2001) have shown that these fishes do not generally have the dentition typical of *Lethrinops* and hence have been included erroneously in the genus in the past.

Taeniolethrinops ECCLES & TREWAVAS, 1989

Etymology: Greek *tainia* = stripe + *lethrinops* (see above); referring tothe characteristic oblique band important in the diagnosis of the genus.
Type species: *Haplochromis praeorbitalis* REGAN, 1922.

Vorhandenseins eines schrägen Streifens vom Nacken zur Schwanzwurzel, wurden die Angehörigen dieser Gattung von *Lethrinops* abgespalten. Ansonsten sind die Zähne, die im Unterkiefer stehen, ähnlich wie bei *Lethrinops* in drei bis fünf Reihen angeordnet. Die äußeren sind vorne zweispitzig und hinten einspitzig. Außerdem sind sie in der äußeren Reihe hinten einwärts gebogen bis zur nächsten Reihe. Mit über 30 cm Gesamtlänge gehören einige Vertreter zu den größten des *Lethrinops*-Komplexes.

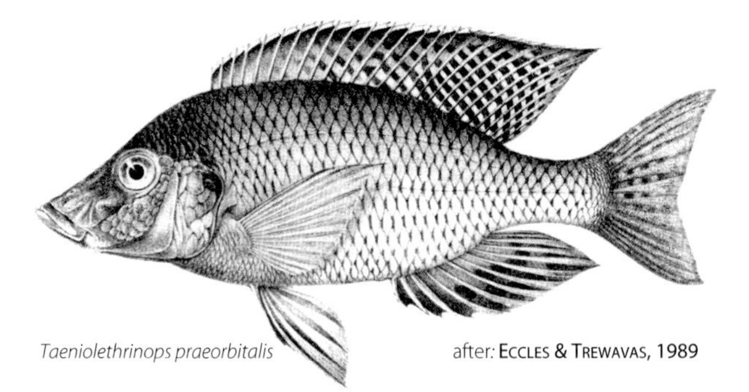

Taeniolethrinops praeorbitalis after: ECCLES & TREWAVAS, 1989

The members of this genus were split off from *Lethrinops* on the basis of a special pattern characteristic, namely the presence of a diagonal band from the nape to the caudal base. That apart, the teeth of the lower jaw are, similarly to in *Lethrinops*, arranged in three to five series, with those of the outer series bicuspid anteriorly and unicuspid posteriorly, and the. outer series curving inwards posteriorly, ending just behind the inner series. With a total length of more than 30 cm, some of these species are the largest members of the "*Lethrinops* complex".

Die schon erwähnte molekulare Untersuchung von HAUSER et al. (1999) ergab, dass alle *Taeniolethrinops*, genau wie die Flachwasser bewohnenden *Lethrinops*, zur Gruppe der „Nicht-Mbunas" gehören.

The molecular studies by Hauser *et al.* (1999) mentioned earlier show that all *Taeniolethrinops*, just like the shallow-water *Lethrinops*, belong to the "non-mbuna" group.

Tramitichromis ECCLES & TREWAVAS, 1989

Etymologie: Lat. 'trames' - Seitenweg + chromis, Name einer anderen Barschgattung zu der früher auch verschiedene Cichliden gezählt wurden; der Name bezieht sich auf die außergewöhnliche Schlundbezahnung, die von der üblichen Bandbreite abweicht (quasi einen anderen Weg einschlägt).
Typusart: *Tilapia brevis* BOULENGER, 1908.

Tramitichromis ECCLES & TREWAVAS, 1989

Etymology: Latin *trames* = a byway + *chromis*, the name of another perciform genus often used to denote "cichlid" for historic reasons; the name refers to "the departure of the pharyngeal jaws from the usual range of structure" (ECCLES & TREWAVAS, 1989)
Type species: *Tilapia brevis* BOULENGER, 1908.

Die Gattung wird durch Besonderheiten der Form des unteren Schlundknochens definiert und enthält Arten mit unterschiedlichem Melaninfarbmuster. Bezüglich der Färbung haben ECCLES & TREWAVAS ausdrücklich der Schlundbezahnung, als ausschlaggebendem Unterscheidungskriterium, den Vorrang gegenüber der Melaninfärbung gegeben und sowohl Arten mit drei Seitenflecken (*T. intermedius*) als auch solche mit schrägem Band vom Nacken bis zum Schwanzstiel (*T. brevis*) zu *Tramitichromis* gestellt. Die Gattung wurde von *Lethrinops* hauptsächlich deshalb abgespalten, weil die Schlundzähne in drei oder mehr Reihen bis zum vorderen Ende des Zahnträgers reichen, der zudem am vorderen Ende des bezahnten Bereiches abgerundet ist. Bei anderen Gattungen reichen auf dem bezahnten Bereich des unteren Schlundknochens nur zwei Reihen von Zähnen bis an das Vorderende; der zudem in einer Spitze endet. Die Unterkieferbezahnung entspricht der von *Lethrinops*.

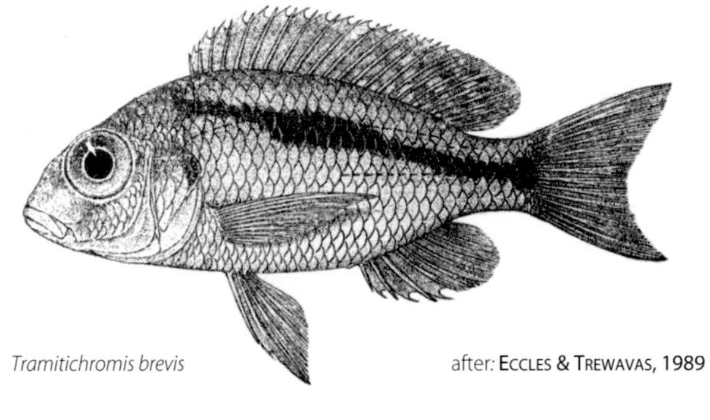

Tramitichromis brevis after: ECCLES & TREWAVAS, 1989

The genus is diagnosed by peculiarities in the form of the lower pharyngeal bone and contains species with different melanin patterns. In favouring the pharyngeal dentition as the critical diagnostic character, Eccles & Trewavas expressly recognise that this is an exception to their general hypothesis regarding the significance of melanin patterns, as both species with three lateral spots (*T. intermedius*) and those with an oblique band from the nape to the caudal peduncle (*T. brevis*) are assigned to *Tramitichromis*. The genus was separated from *Lethrinops* mainly because the pharyngeal teeth extend in three or more rows to the anterior end of the toothed area, which in addition is rounded. In other genera there are only two rows of teeth extending to the anterior end of the lower pharyngeal bone, which ends in a point. The lower jaw dentition resembles that of *Lethrinops*.

NGATUNGA hat in einer nicht veröffentlichten Doktorarbeit dargestellt, dass *Tramitichromis* aufgrund der DNA ebenfalls näher mit den Flachwasser-Lethrinops verwandt sind und damit in die verwandtschaftliche Gruppe der „Nicht-Mbunas" gehören.

In an unpublished Ph.D. thesis NGATUNGA suggests that, on the basis of DNA, *Tramitichromis* are again more closely related to the shallow-water *Lethrinops* and hence belong to the "non-mbuna" phyletic group.

A05748-4 *Astatotilapia calliptera* (GÜNTHER, 1894)
Photographed specimen is from Lake Malawi
Lake Malawi , W, 17 cm

photo: E. Schraml

A05747-4 *Astatotilapia calliptera* (GÜNTHER, 1894)
Lakes Malawi, Chiuta and Chilwa; Lower Zambezi, Buzi, Pungwe & Save River systems; W, B, 17 cm (origin of photographed specimen unknown)

photo: E. Schraml

A05747-4 *Astatotilapia calliptera* (GÜNTHER, 1894)
Lakes Malawi, Chiuta and Chilwa; Lower Zambezi, Buzi, Pungwe & Save River systems; W, B, 17 cm (origin of photographed specimen unknown)

photo: E. Schraml

A05750-4 *Astatotilapia tweddlei* JACKSON, 1985 *

Lakes Chilwa and Chiuta and in flowing rivers; W, B, 12 cm

photo: E. Schraml

A05750-4 *Astatotilapia tweddlei* JACKSON, 1985 *

Lakes Chilwa and Chiuta and in flowing rivers; W, B, 12 cm

photo: E. Schraml

* Die Art wird hier gezeigt, weil sie häufig mit *Astatotilapia calliptera* verwechselt wird und in den Seen Chilwa und Chiuta syntop mit *A. calliptera* lebt.
* This species is depicted here, because it is often confused with *Astatotilapia calliptera* and lives syntopically with *A. calliptera* in the Lakes Chilwa and Chiuta.

A00450-4 *Alticorpus* sp. "Deep"

Lake Malawi: SE-Arm, 52-102 m depth, W, 16 cm

photo: G. Turner

A00451-4 *Alticorpus geoffreyi* SNOEKS & WALAPA, 2004

Lake Malawi: 54-128 m depth, W, 20 cm

photo: G. Turner

A00453-4 *Alticorpus mentale* STAUFFER & MCKAYE, 1988

Lake Malawi: 18-130 m depth, W, 25 cm

photo: M. Smith

A00453-4 *Alticorpus mentale* STAUFFER & MCKAYE, 1988

Lake Malawi: 18-130 m depth, W, 25 cm

photo: A. Spreinat

A00454-4 *Alticorpus peterdaviesi* (BURGESS & AXELROD, 1973)
(drwaing shows the holotype)
Lake Malawi: 60-128 m depth, W, 16 cm

drawing: E. Schraml

A00455-4 *Alticorpus peterdaviesi* (BURGESS & AXELROD, 1973)
(= *Alticorpus pectinatum* STAUFFER & MCKAYE, 1988*)
Lake Malawi: 60-128 m depth, W, 16 cm

drawing: E. Schraml

A00456-4 *Alticorpus macrocleithrum* (STAUFFER & MCKAYE, 1985)

Lake Malawi: 35-128 m depth, W, 18 cm

photo: G. Turner

A00457-3 *Alticorpus profundicola* STAUFFER & MCKAYE, 1988

Lake Malawi: 90-159 m depth, W, 15 cm

photo: G. Turner

*Drawing shows the paratye of *Alticorpus peterdaviesi*, which was chosen by STAUFFER &MCKAYE as the holotype of their species *Alticorpus pectinatum*, which is considered as synonym of *A. peterdaviesi* by SNOEKS &WALAPA, 2004)

A00458-4 *Alticorpus* sp. "Bicusp Bis"

Lake Malawi: Senga Bay; W, 14 cm

photo: Africamuseum Tervuren

A00459-4 *Alticorpus* sp. "Deep Bicusp"

Lake Malawi: Nkhotakota; W, 12 cm

photo: Africamuseum Tervuren

A00460-4 *Alticorpus* sp. "Bicusp Small Scale"

Lake Malawi: Senga Bay; W, 13 cm

photo: Africamuseum Tervuren

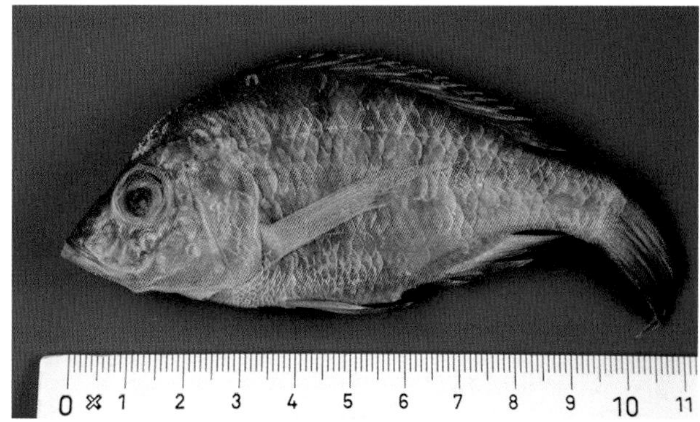

A00461-4 *Alticorpus* sp. "Mentale Bicusp"

Lake Malawi: Senga Bay; W, 11 cm

photo: Africamuseum Tervuren

A00462-4 *Alticorpus* sp. "Bicusp Bis"

Lake Malawi: Nkhata Bay; 14 cm

photo: Africamuseum Tervuren

A05994-4 *Aulonocara/Otopharynx* sp. "Brevirostris Deep"*
formerly placed in *Trematocranus*
Lake Malawi: N of Monkey Bay; 10 cm

  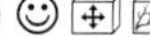  

photo: G. Turner

A05993-4 *Aulonocara/Otopharynx brevirostris* (Trewavas, 1935)*
formerly placed in *Trematocranus*
Lake Malawi: S of Boadzulu Isl.; 10 cm

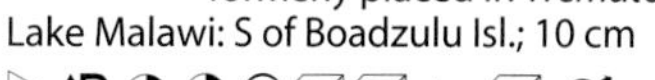 

photo: G. Turner

A05993-4 *Aulonocara/Otopharynx brevirostris* (Trewavas, 1935)*
lectotyp BMNH 1935.6.14.2224-2225; formerly *Trematocranus*
Lake Malawi: 'Bar House' SE Arm of the lake; 10 cm

photo: E. Schraml

*Es ist derzeit unklar und wird kontrovers diskutiert, in welche Gattung diese Arten gehören.
**It is actually unclear and still under discussion in which genus these species should be placed.*

A05786-4 *Aulonocara aquilonium* Konings, 1995

Lake Malawi: Mdoka (north of Chilumba), W, 11 cm

photo: A. Konings

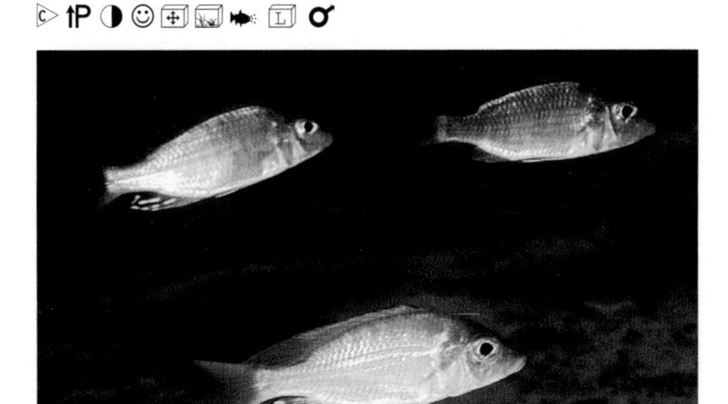

A05786-4 *Aulonocara aquilonium* Konings, 1995

Lake Malawi: Mdoka (north of Chilumba), W, 11 cm

photo: A. Konings

A05791-4 *Aulonocara auditor* (Trewavas, 1935)
Syntype BMNH 1935.6.14.2238
Lake Malawi: Vua, W pres., 10 cm

photo: E. Schraml

A05793-4 *Aulonocara brevinidus* Konings, 1995

Lake Malawi: Chiloelo, W, 12 cm

photo: A. Konings

A05794-4 *Aulonocara brevinidus* Konings, 1995

Lake Malawi: Tansania: Lupono (Mbamba Bay), W, 12 cm

photo: A. Spreinat

A05796-4 *Aulonocara brevinidus* KONINGS, 1995

Lake Malawi: Wikihi, W, 12 cm

photo: A. Konings

A05792-4 *Aulonocara brevinidus* KONINGS, 1995

Lake Malawi: W, 12 cm

photo: H. J. Mayland

A05792-4 *Aulonocara brevinidus* Konings, 1995

Lake Malawi: W, 12 cm

photo: A. Spreinat

A05792-4 *Aulonocara brevinidus* Konings, 1995

Lake Malawi: W, 12 cm

photo: Verduijn Cichl./ES

A05797-4 *Aulonocara* sp. "Blue Orange"

Lake Malawi: SE-Arm, n. Boadzulu, W, 11 cm

photo: G. Turner

A05798-4 *Aulonocara* sp. "Deep Yellow"

Lake Malawi: Maleri Isl., W, 9 cm

photo: G. Turner

A05799-4 *Aulonocara* sp. "Yellow"

Lake Malawi: Mpemba, W, 8 cm

photo: G. Turner

A05801-4 *Aulonocara* sp. "Orange"

Lake Malawi: Mpemba, Michesi, W, 9.5 cm

photo: G. Turner

A05803-4 *Aulonocara stonemani* (Burgess & Axelrod, 1973)

Lake Malawi: Monkey Bay, W, 7 cm

photo: G. Turner

A05804-4 *Aulonocara* sp. "Dark Stripe"

Lake Malawi: Boadzulu Isl., W, 8 cm

photo: G. Turner

A05806-4 *Aulonocara* sp. "Minutus"

Lake Malawi: Monkey Bay, W, 7 cm

photo: G. Turner

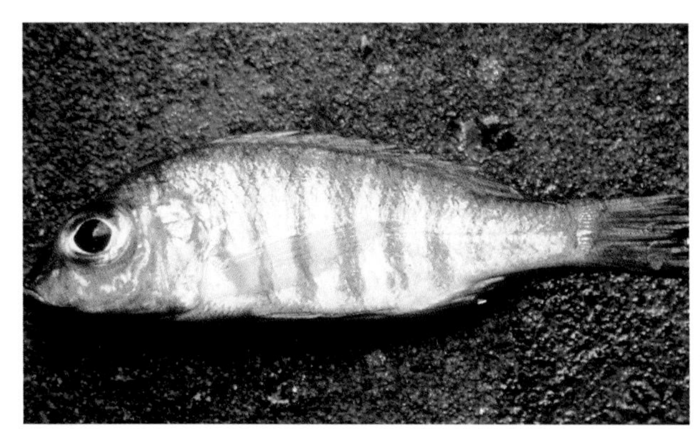

A05807-4 *Aulonocara* sp. "Pyramid"

Lake Malawi: Boadzulu Isl.-Monkey Bay, W, 12 cm

photo: G. Turner

A05808 *Aulonocara* (?) sp. "Nyassae Mumbo"

Lake Malawi: Mumbo Isl., W, ? cm

photo: Ad Konings

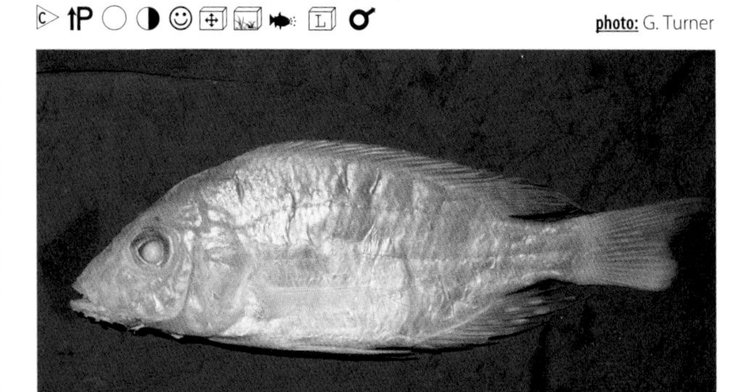

A05809-4 *Aulonocara guentheri* Eccles, 1989
Holotype BMNH 1921.9.6.221
Lake Malawi: unknown, W, 13 cm

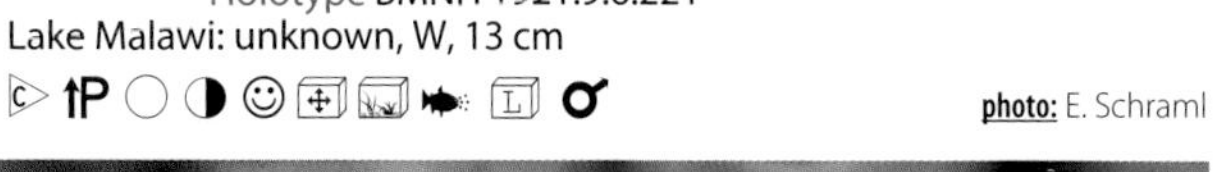

photo: E. Schraml

A05812-4 *Aulonocara guentheri* Eccles, 1989

Lake Malawi: Senga Bay, W, 13 cm

photo: Ad Konings

A05812-4 *Aulonocara guentheri* ECCLES, 1989

Lake Malawi: Senga Bay, W, 13 cm

♂ **photo:** A. Spreinat

A05812-4 *Aulonocara guentheri* ECCLES, 1989

Lake Malawi: Senga Bay, W, 13 cm

♀ **photo:** A. Spreinat

A05813-4 *Aulonocara guentheri* ECCLES, 1989

Lake Malawi: Thumbi East Isl., W, 13 cm

♂ **photo:** Ad Konings

A05814-4 *Aulonocara* cf. *guentheri*

Lake Malawi: unknown, W, 13 cm

♂ **photo:** H. J. Mayland

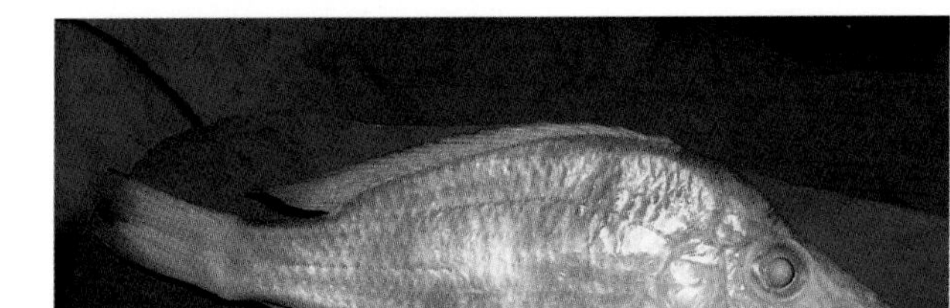

A05835-4 *Aulonocara macrochir* TREWAVAS, 1935 BMNH 1986.2.5.7-8
(acc. KONINGS a synonym of *A. rostratum*)
Lake Malawi: Monkey Bay, W, 18 cm

photo: E. Schraml

A05836-4 *Aulonocara* cf. *macrochir*

Lake Malawi: SE-Arm, W, 18 cm

♂ **photo:** G. Turner

A- *Aulonocara rostratum* TREWAVAS, 1935

Lake Malawi: 15-30 m depth, W, 18 cm

♂ **photo:** E. Schraml

A- *Aulonocara rostratum* TREWAVAS, 1935

Lake Malawi: 15-30 m depth, W, 18 cm

♂ **photo:** A.Spreinat

A05862-4 *Aulonocara rostratum* TREWAVAS, 1935

Lake Malawi: 15-30 m depth, W, 18 cm

♂

photo: H. J. Mayland

A05862-4 *Aulonocara rostratum* TREWAVAS, 1935

Lake Malawi: 15-30 m depth, W, 18 cm

♂

photo: Mal-Ta-Vi/E.S.

A05862-4 *Aulonocara rostratum* TREWAVAS, 1935

Lake Malawi: 15-30 m depth, W, 18 cm

♀

photo: A. Spreinat

A05817-4 *Aulonocara* sp. "Lupingu" fide SPREINAT
= *A. gertrudae* fide KONINGS
Lake Malawi: Lupingu (Tan.), W, 13 cm

♂

photo: A. Spreinat

A05817-4 *Aulonocara gertrudae* KONINGS, 1995
= *A.* sp. Lupingu fide SPREINAT
Lake Malawi: Lupingu (Tan.), W, 13 cm

♀

photo: Ad Konings

A05818-4 *Aulonocara* sp. "Lupingu" fide SPREINAT
= *A. gertrudae* fide KONINGS
Lake Malawi: Lumbira (Tan.), W, 13 cm

photo: A. Spreinat

A05819-4 *Aulonocara* sp. "Trematocranus Masinje"

Lake Malawi: Gome, W, 15 cm

photo: Ad Konings

A05821-4 *Aulonocara* sp. "Lupingu" fide SPREINAT
= *Aul. gertrudae* fide KONINGS
Lake Malawi: Makonde (Tan.), W, 13 cm
♂ **photo:** A. Spreinat

A05821-4 *Aulonocara* sp. "Lupingu" fide SPREINAT
= *Aul. gertrudae* fide KONINGS
Lake Malawi: Makonde (Tan.), W, 13 cm
♀ **photo:** A. Spreinat

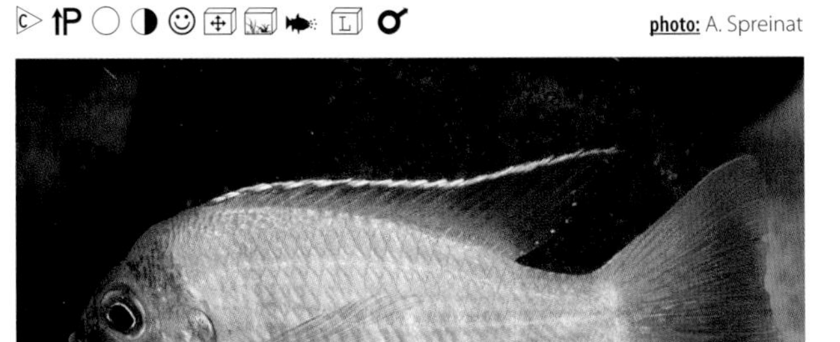

A05817-4 *Aulonocara gertrudae* KONINGS, 1995 fide KONINGS
= *A.* sp. Lupingu fide SPREINAT
Lake Malawi: Lupingu (Tan.), W, 13 cm
♂ **photo:** J. Steves

A05822-4 *Aulonocara gertrudae* KONINGS, 1995 fide KONINGS
= *A.* sp. Lupingu fide SPREINAT
Lake Malawi: Lundu (Tan.), W, 13 cm
♂ **photo:** Ad Konings

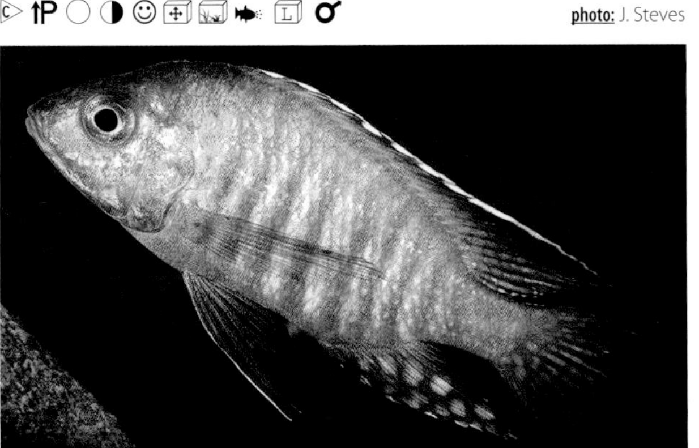

A05823-4 *Aulonocara gertrudae* KONINGS, 1995 fide KONINGS
= *A.* sp. Lupingu fide SPREINAT
Lake Malawi: Nkanda (Tan.), W, 13 cm

♂ **photo:** Ad Konings

A05824-4 *Aulonocara gertrudae* KONINGS, 1995 fide KONINGS
= *A.* sp. Lupingu fide SPREINAT
Lake Malawi: Lumessi (Mos.), W, 13 cm
♂ **photo:** Ad Konings

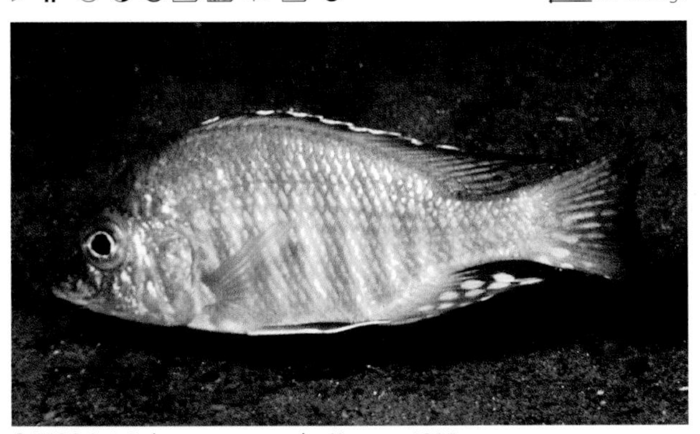

A05826-4 *Aulonocara gertrudae* KONINGS, 1995

Lake Malawi: Narungu, W, 13 cm
♂ **photo:** Ad Konings

A05826-4 *Aulonocara gertrudae* KONINGS, 1995

Lake Malawi: Narungu, W, 13 cm
♀ **photo:** Ad Konings

A05805-4 *Aulonocara gertrudae* Konings, 1995

Lake Malawi: Masinje, W, 13 cm

photo: Ad Konings

A05805-4 *Aulonocara gertrudae* Konings, 1995

Lake Malawi: W, 13 cm

photo: E. Schraml

A05827-4 *Aulonocara gertrudae* Konings, 1995

Lake Malawi: Chikala (Mos.), W, 13 cm

photo: A. Spreinat

A05828-4 *Aulonocara gertrudae* Konings, 1995

Lake Malawi: Makanjila, W, 13 cm

photo: A. Spreinat

A05805-4 *Aulonocara gertrudae* Konings, 1995

Lake Malawi: Masinje, W, 13 cm

photo: A. Spreinat

A05805-4 *Aulonocara gertrudae* KONINGS, 1995

Lake Malawi: Masinje, W, 13 cm

photo: A. Spreinat

A05829-4 *Aulonocara gertrudae* KONINGS, 1995

Lake Malawi: Fort Maguire, Makanjila, W, 13 cm

photo: A. Spreinat

A05863-4 *Aulonocara saulosi* MEYER, RIEHL & ZETZSCHE, 1987

Lake Malawi: B, 11 cm

photo: Nakano/A.C.S.

A05831-4 *Aulonocara saulosi* MEYER, RIEHL & ZETZSCHE, 1987

Lake Malawi: N'tekete, Makanjila, W, 11 cm

photo: A. Spreinat

A05831-4 *Aulonocara saulosi* MEYER, RIEHL & ZETZSCHE, 1987

Lake Malawi: N'tekete, Makanjila, W, 11 cm

photo: A. Spreinat

A05863-4 *Aulonocara saulosi* MEYER, RIEHL & ZETZSCHE, 1987

Lake Malawi: 11 cm

♂ **photo:** A. Spreinat

A05863-5 *Aulonocara saulosi* MEYER, RIEHL & ZETZSCHE, 1987

Lake Malawi: 11 cm

♂ **photo:** A. Spreinat

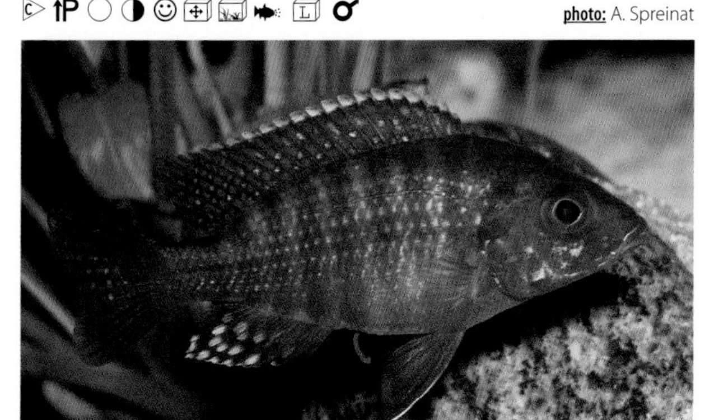

A05863-3 *Aulonocara saulosi* MEYER, RIEHL & ZETZSCHE, 1987

Lake Malawi: 11 cm

♂ **photo:** A. Spreinat

A05863-4 *Aulonocara saulosi* MEYER, RIEHL & ZETZSCHE, 1987

Lake Malawi: B, 11 cm

♂ **photo:** Nakano/A.C.S.

A05832-4 *Aulonocara saulosi* MEYER, RIEHL & ZETZSCHE, 1987

Lake Malawi: Membe Pt., Likoma, W, 11 cm

♂ **photo:** A. Spreinat

A05833-4 *Aulonocara saulosi* MEYER, RIEHL & ZETZSCHE, 1987

Lake Malawi: Hai Reef (Tan.), W, 11 cm

♀ **photo:** A. Spreinat

A05810-4 *Aulonocara hansbaenschi* MEYER, RIEHL & ZETZSCHE, 1987
= *A. stuartgranti* fide KONINGS
Lake Malawi: B, 12 cm

♂ **photo:** E. Schraml

A05834-4 *Aulonocara hansbaenschi* MEYER, RIEHL & ZETZSCHE, 1987
= *A. stuartgranti* fide KONINGS
Lake Malawi: btw. Fort Maguire and Masinje, W, 12 cm

♀ **photo:** E. Schraml

A05810-4 *Aulonocara hansbaenschi* Meyer, Riehl & Zetzsche, 1987
= *A. stuartgranti* fide Konings
Lake Malawi: B, 12 cm

photo: H. J. Mayland

A05886-5 *Aulonocara hansbaenschi* Meyer, Riehl & Zetzsche, 1987
Albino, = *A. stuartgranti* fide Konings
Lake Malawi: Z, 12 cm

photo: Nakano/A.C.S.

A05834-5 *Aulonocara hansbaenschi* MEYER, RIEHL & ZETZSCHE, 1987
= *A. stuartgranti* fide KONINGS
Lake Malawi: btw. Fort Maguire and Masinje, W, 12 cm
♂ **photo:** W. van der Elst

A05834-4 *Aulonocara hansbaenschi* MEYER, RIEHL & ZETZSCHE, 1987
= *A. stuartgranti* fide KONINGS
Lake Malawi: btw. Fort Maguire and Masinje, W, 12 cm
♀ **photo:** E. Schraml

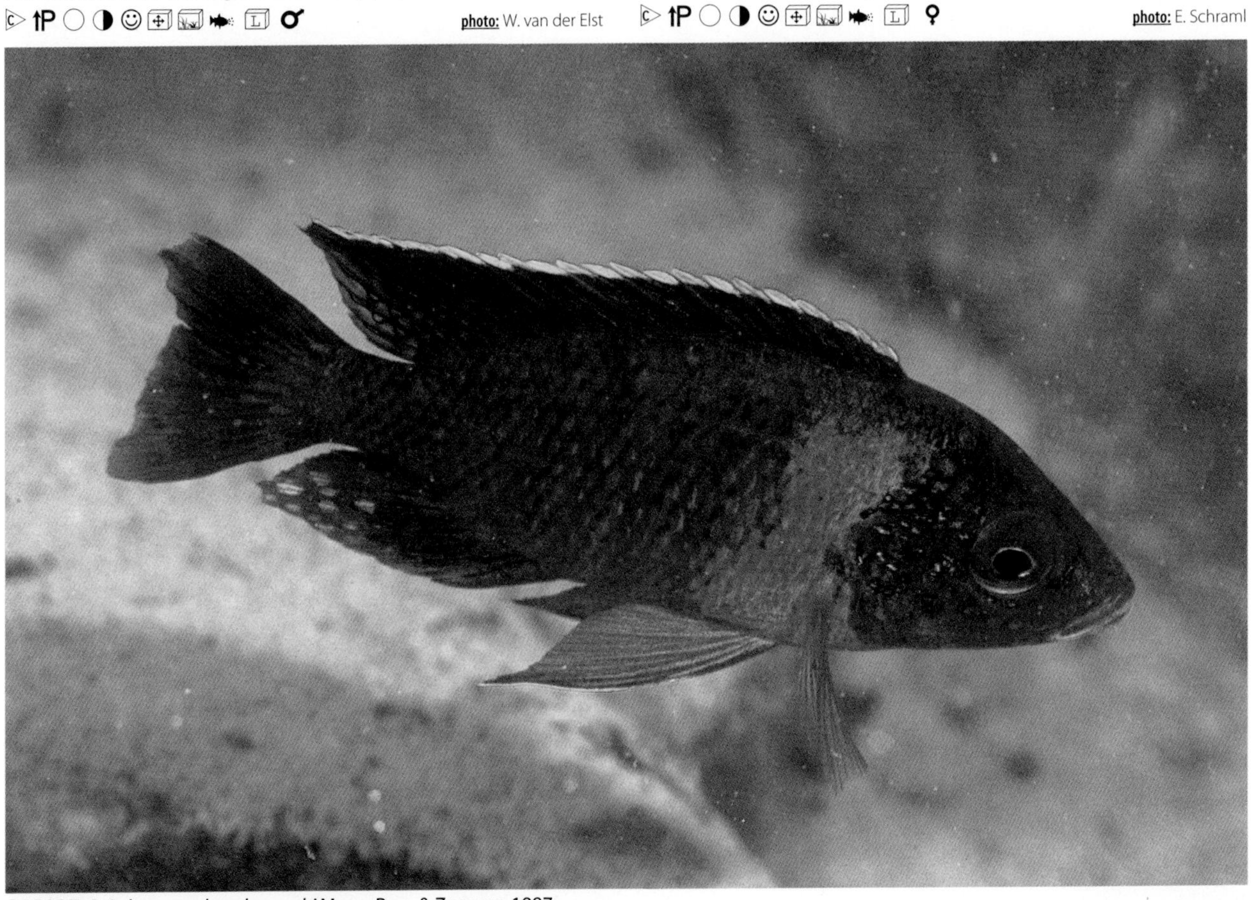

A05837-4 *Aulonocara hansbaenschi* MEYER, RIEHL & ZETZSCHE, 1987
= *A. stuartgranti* fide KONINGS
Lake Malawi: Jilambo (Mos.), W, 12 cm

♂ **photo:** A. Spreinat

A05838-4 *Aulonocara hansbaenschi* MEYER, RIEHL & ZETZSCHE, 1987
= *A. stuartgranti* fide KONINGS
Lake Malawi: Ngumbe Rocks (Mos.), W, 12 cm
♂ **photo:** A. Spreinat

A05838-4 *Aulonocara hansbaenschi* MEYER, RIEHL & ZETZSCHE, 1987
= *A. stuartgranti* fide KONINGS
Lake Malawi: Ngumbe Rocks (Mos.), W, 12 cm
♀ **photo:** A. Spreinat

Aulonocara hansbaenschi MEYER, RIEHL & ZETZSCHE, 1987
Fressend im natürlichen Lebensraum / feeding in it´s natural habitat.
Lake Malawi: Minga Bay (Mos.), W, 12 cm

A05834-5 *Aulonocara hansbaenschi* MEYER, RIEHL & ZETZSCHE, 1987
= *A. stuartgranti* fide KONINGS
Lake Malawi: btw. Fort Maguire and Masinje, W, 12 cm

♂ **photo:** E. Schraml

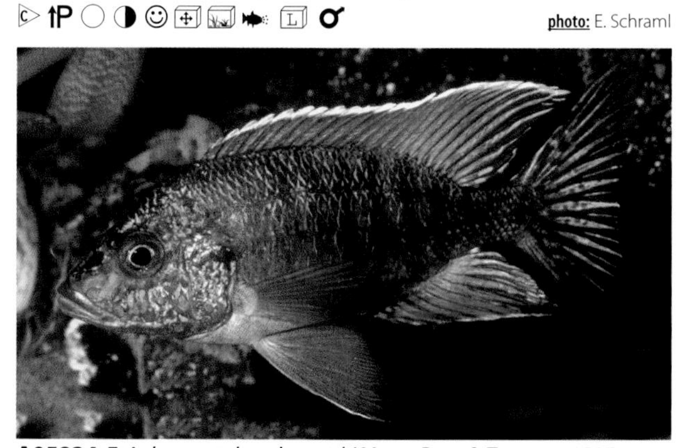

A05834-5 *Aulonocara hansbaenschi* MEYER, RIEHL & ZETZSCHE, 1987
= *A. stuartgranti* fide KONINGS
Lake Malawi: btw. Fort Maguire and Masinje, W, 12 cm

photo: W. van der Elst

A05837-4 *Aulonocara hansbaenschi* MEYER, RIEHL & ZETZSCHE, 1987
= *A. stuartgranti* fide KONINGS
Lake Malawi: Jilambo (Mos.), W, 12 cm

♀ **photo:** A. Spreinat

A05810-3 *Aulonocara hansbaenschi* MEYER, RIEHL & ZETZSCHE, 1987
= *A. stuartgranti* fide KONINGS
Lake Malawi: B, 12 cm

♂ **photo:** Nakano/A.C.S.

A05834-4 *Aulonocara hansbaenschi* Meyer, Riehl & Zetzsche, 1987
= *A. stuartgranti* fide Konings
Lake Malawi: btw. Fort Maguire and Masinje, W, 12 cm

♂ **photo:** E. Schraml

A05834-4 *Aulonocara hansbaenschi* Meyer, Riehl & Zetzsche, 1987
= *A. stuartgranti* fide Konings
Lake Malawi: btw. Fort Maguire and Masinje, W, 12 cm

♂ **photo:** E. Schraml

A05839-4 *Aulonocara hansbaenschi* Meyer, Riehl & Zetzsche, 1987
Population from Cobue, introduced near Cape Maclear
Lake Malawi: Thumbi West Isl./Cobue, W, 12 cm

♂ **photo:** B. Migge / Archiv A.C.S.

A05839-4 *Aulonocara hansbaenschi* Meyer, Riehl & Zetzsche, 1987
Population from Cobue, introduced near Cape Maclear
Lake Malawi: Thumbi West Isl./Cobue, W, 12 cm

♂ **photo:** Piednoir

A05839-5 *Aulonocara hansbaenschi* Meyer, Riehl & Zetzsche, 1987
Population from Cobue, introduced near Cape Maclear
Lake Malawi: Thumbi West Isl./Cobue, W, 12 cm

♂ **photo:** A. Spreinat

A05839-4 *Aulonocara hansbaenschi* Meyer, Riehl & Zetzsche, 1987
Population from Cobue, introduced near Cape Maclear
Lake Malawi: Thumbi West Isl./Cobue, W, 12 cm

♀ **photo:** A. Spreinat

A05841-4 *Aulonocara hansbaenschi* Meyer, Riehl & Zetzsche, 1987
= *A. stuartgranti* fide Konings
Lake Malawi: Cobue, W, 12 cm

♂ **photo:** W. van der Elst

A05841-4 *Aulonocara hansbaenschi* Meyer, Riehl & Zetzsche, 1987
= *A. stuartgranti* fide Konings
Lake Malawi: Cobue, W, 12 cm

♀ **photo:** A. Spreinat

A05922-4 *Aulonocara stuartgranti* MEYER & RIEHL, 1985

Lake Malawi: Mdoka, W, 11 cm

photo: E. Schraml

A05916-4 *Aulonocara stuartgranti* MEYER & RIEHL, 1985

Lake Malawi: Chitendi Isl., Chilumba, W, 11 cm

photo: A. Spreinat

A05790-4 *Aulonocara stuartgranti* MEYER & RIEHL, 1985

Lake Malawi: Chilumba, W, 11 cm
♂ photo: A. Spreinat

A05790-4 *Aulonocara stuartgranti* MEYER & RIEHL, 1985

Lake Malawi: Chilumba, W, 11 cm
♀ photo: E. Schraml

A05790-4 *Aulonocara stuartgranti* MEYER & RIEHL, 1985

Lake Malawi: Chilumba, W, 11 cm
♂ photo: E. Schraml

A05790-4 *Aulonocara stuartgranti* MEYER & RIEHL, 1985

Lake Malawi: Chilumba, W, 11 cm
♀ photo: A. Spreinat

A05790-4 *Aulonocara stuartgranti* MEYER & RIEHL, 1985

Lake Malawi: Chilumba, W, 11 cm
♂ photo: E. Schraml

A05790-4 *Aulonocara stuartgranti* MEYER & RIEHL, 1985

Lake Malawi: Chilumba, W, 11 cm
♂ photo: E. Schraml

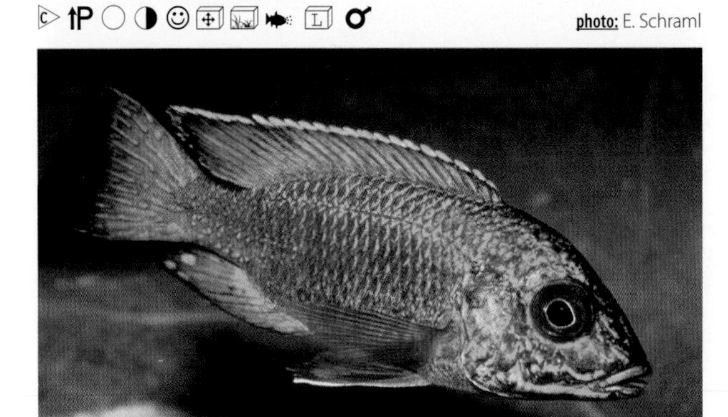

A05906-4 *Aulonocara stuartgranti* MEYER & RIEHL, 1985

Lake Malawi: Ngara, W, 11 cm
♂ photo: W. van der Elst

A05906-4 *Aulonocara stuartgranti* MEYER & RIEHL, 1985

Lake Malawi: Ngara, W, 11 cm
♂ photo: E. Schraml

A05907-4 *Aulonocara stuartgranti* MEYER & RIEHL, 1985
"Maison"
Lake Malawi: Chitimba Bay, W, 13 cm

photo: W. van der Elst

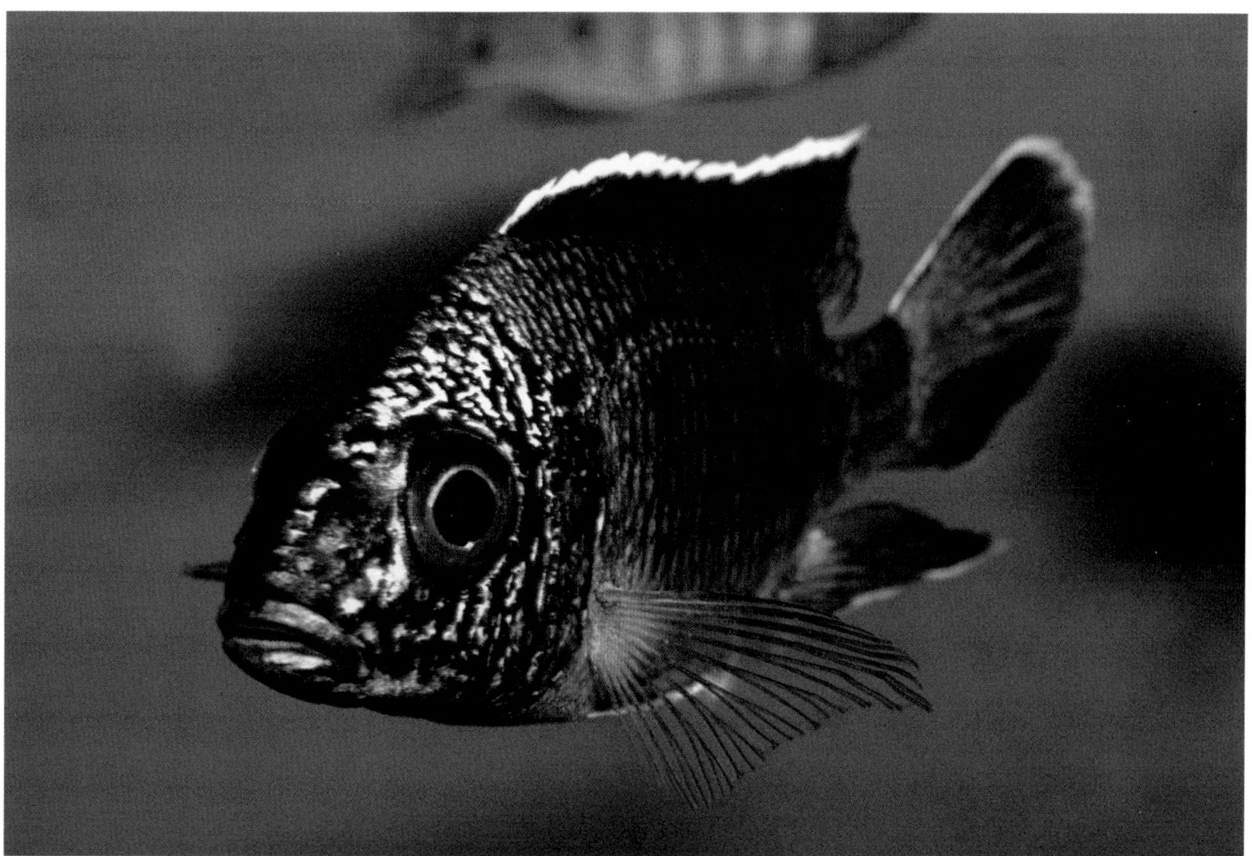

A05907-4 *Aulonocara stuartgranti* MEYER & RIEHL, 1985
"Maison"
Lake Malawi: Chitimba Bay, W, 13 cm

photo: W. van der Elst

A05905-4 *Aulonocara stuartgranti* MEYER & RIEHL, 1985
"Maulana"
Lake Malawi: Chitimba Bay, W, 9-10 cm

photo: E. Schraml

A05908-4 *Aulonocara* sp. "Chadagha"
= *Aulonocara stuartgranti* fide KONINGS
Lake Malawi: Chadagha, W, 11 cm

photo: Ad Konings

A05909-4 *Aulonocara* sp. "Ntumba"
= *Aulonocara stuartgranti* fide Konings
Lake Malawi: Ntumba (Mos.), W, 10 cm
♂

photo: A. Konings

A05909-4 *Aulonocara* sp. "Ntumba"
Aulonocara stuartgranti Meyer & Riehl, 1985 fide Konings
Lake Malawi: Ntumba (Mos.), W, 10 cm
♀

photo: Ad Konings

Aufbruch zum Fischfang.
Start of a fishing trip.

photo: Hans. J. Mayland

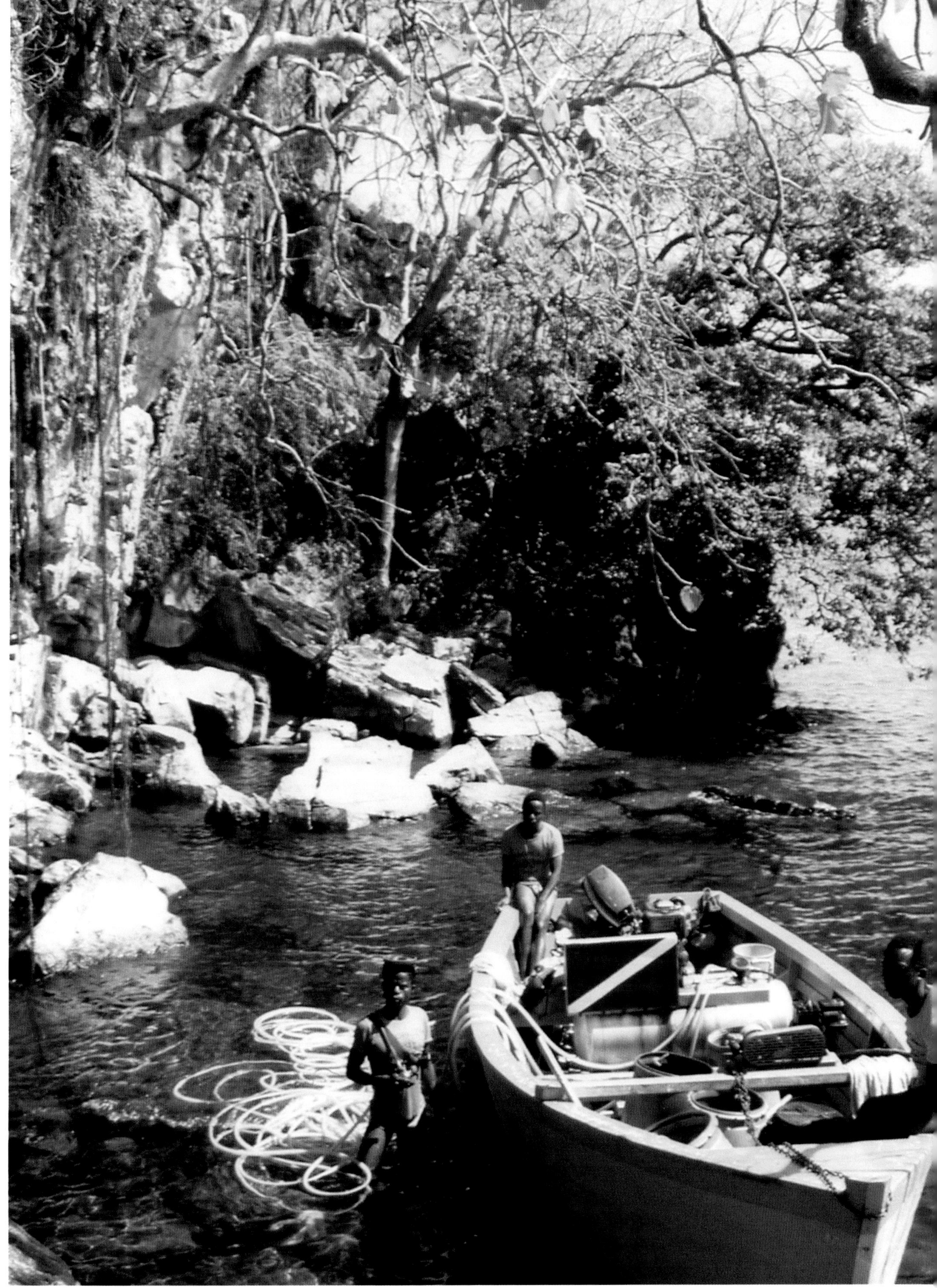

Das Fischfangteam bei der Arbeit.
The fishermen at work.

photo: Hans. J. Mayland

A05917-4 *Aulonocara koningsi* TAWIL, 2003

Lake Malawi: Mbenji Isl., W, 11 cm

photo: H. J. Mayland

A05917-4 *Aulonocara koningsi* TAWIL, 2003

Lake Malawi: Mbenji Isl., W, 11 cm

photo: Ad Konings

A05917-4 *Aulonocara koningsi* TAWIL, 2003

Lake Malawi: Mbenji Isl., W, 11 cm

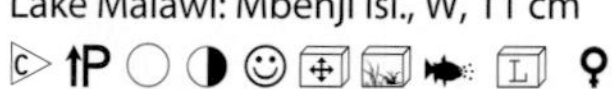

photo: Ad Konings

A05917-4 *Aulonocara koningsi* TAWIL, 2003

Lake Malawi: Mbenji Isl., W, 11 cm

photo: A. Spreinat

A05917-4 *Aulonocara koningsi* TAWIL, 2003

Lake Malawi: Mbenji Isl., W, 11 cm

photo: A. Spreinat

A05911-4 *Aulonocara koningsi* Tawil, 2003

Lake Malawi: Mpandi Reef, W, 11 cm

photo: H. J. Mayland

A05865-4 *Aulonocara* sp. "Blue Neon"
= *A. stuartgranti* fide Konings/ = *A. steveni* fide Spreinat
Lake Malawi: Undu Point (Tan.), W, 9 cm

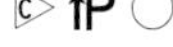

photo: Sch. Nakano/A.C.S.

A05866-4 *Aulonocara* sp. "Blue Neon"
= *A. stuartgranti* fide Konings/ = *A. steveni* fide Spreinat
Lake Malawi: Hai Reef (Tan.), W, 9 cm

photo: A. Spreinat

A05866-4 *Aulonocara* sp. "Blue Neon"
= *A. stuartgranti* fide Konings/ = *A. steveni* fide Spreinat
Lake Malawi: Hai Reef (Tan.), W, 9 cm

photo: A. Spreinat

A05865-4 *Aulonocara* sp. "Blue Neon"
= *A. stuartgranti* fide Konings/ = *A. steveni* fide Spreinat
Lake Malawi: Undu Point (Tan.), W, 9 cm

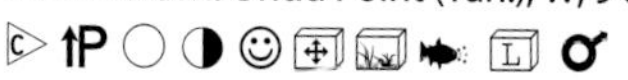

photo: A. Spreinat

A05865-4 *Aulonocara* sp. "Blue Neon"
= *A. stuartgranti* fide Konings/ = *A. steveni* fide Spreinat
Lake Malawi: Undu Point (Tan.), W, 9 cm

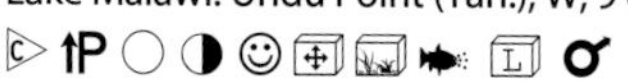

photo: A. Spreinat

A05865-4 *Aulonocara* sp. "Blue Neon"
= *A. stuartgranti* fide Konings/ = *A. steveni* fide Spreinat
Lake Malawi: Undu Point (Tan.), W, 9 cm

photo: A. Spreinat

A05867-4 *Aulonocara* sp. "Steveni Tanzania"
= *A. stuartgranti* fide Konings/ = *A. steveni* fide Spreinat
Lake Malawi: Njambe Isl. (Tan.), W, 11 cm

photo: A. Spreinat

A05868-4 *Aulonocara* sp. "Steveni Tanzania"
= *A. stuartgranti* fide Konings/ = *A. steveni* fide Spreinat
Lake Malawi: Tumbi Reef (Tan.), W, 11 cm

photo: A. Spreinat

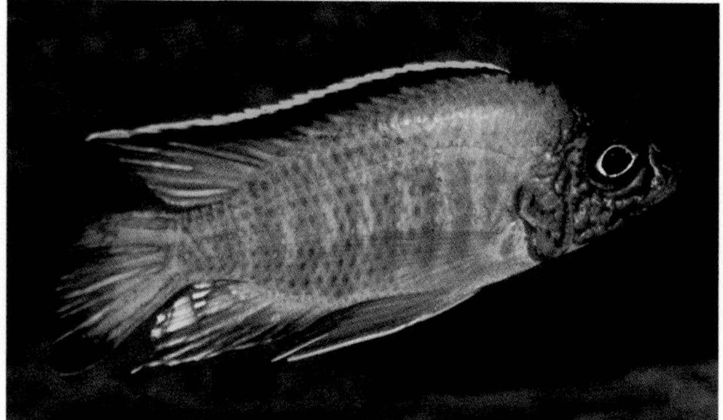

A05869-4 *Aulonocara* sp. "Steveni Tanzania"
= *A. stuartgranti* fide Konings/ = *A. steveni* fide Spreinat
Lake Malawi: Mbahwa Isl. (Tan.), W, 11 cm

photo: A. Spreinat

A05870-4 *Aulonocara* sp. "Steveni Tanzania"
= *A. stuartgranti* fide KONINGS/ = *A. steveni* fide SPREINAT
Lake Malawi: , W, 11 cm

photo: A. Spreinat

A05871-4 *Aulonocara* sp. "Steveni Tanzania"
= *A. stuartgranti* fide KONINGS/ = *A. steveni* fide SPREINAT
Lake Malawi: Lundo Isl. (Tan.), W, 9-11 cm

photo: A. Spreinat

A05872-4 *Aulonocara* sp. "Steveni Tanzania"
= *A. stuartgranti* fide KONINGS/ = *A. steveni* fide SPREINAT
Lake Malawi: Mbamba Bay (Tan.), W, 11 cm

photo: A. Spreinat

A05873-4 *Aulonocara steveni* MEYER, RIEHL & ZETZSCHE, 1987
= *A. stuartgranti* fide KONINGS
Lake Malawi: Kande Isl. (= type locality of *A. steveni*), W, 11 cm

photo: A. Spreinat

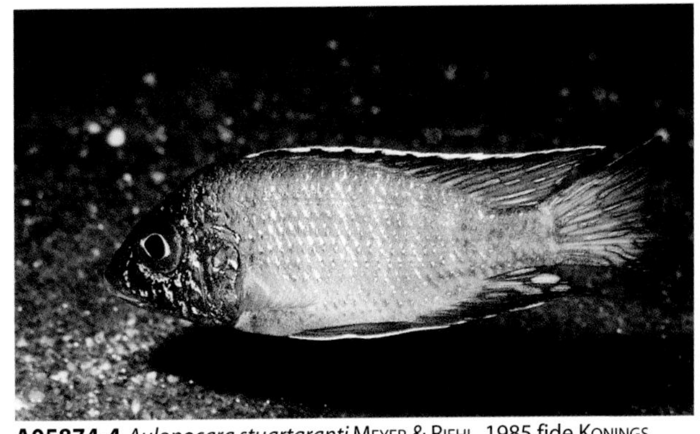

A05874-4 *Aulonocara stuartgranti* MEYER & RIEHL, 1985 fide KONINGS
= *A. steveni* fide SPREINAT
Lake Malawi: Ruarwe, W, 11 cm

photo: Ad Konings

A05876-4 *Aulonocara steveni* Meyer, Riehl & Zetzsche, 1987
= *A. stuartgranti* fide Konings
Lake Malawi: Usisya, W, 11 cm

photo: E. Schraml

A05877-4 *Aulonocara steveni* Meyer, Riehl & Zetzsche, 1987
= *A. stuartgranti* fide Konings
Lake Malawi: 11 cm

photo: Piednoir

A05876-4 *Aulonocara steveni* MEYER, RIEHL & ZETZSCHE, 1987
= *A. stuartgranti* fide KONINGS
Lake Malawi: Usisya, W, 11 cm

    ♂

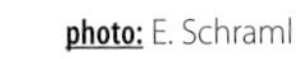 photo: E. Schraml

A05876-4 *Aulonocara steveni* MEYER, RIEHL & ZETZSCHE, 1987
= *A. stuartgranti* fide KONINGS
Lake Malawi: Usisya, W, 11 cm

    ♀

photo: E. Schraml

A05878-4 *Aulonocara steveni* MEYER, RIEHL & ZETZSCHE, 1987
Var. "Black & Gold", = *A. stuartgranti* fide KONINGS
Lake Malawi: ?, W, 11 cm

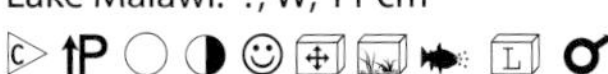 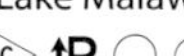    ♂

photo: E. Schraml

A05878-4 *Aulonocara steveni* MEYER, RIEHL & ZETZSCHE, 1987
Var. "Black & Gold", = *A. stuartgranti* fide KONINGS
Lake Malawi: ?, W, 11 cm

    ♀

photo: E. Schraml

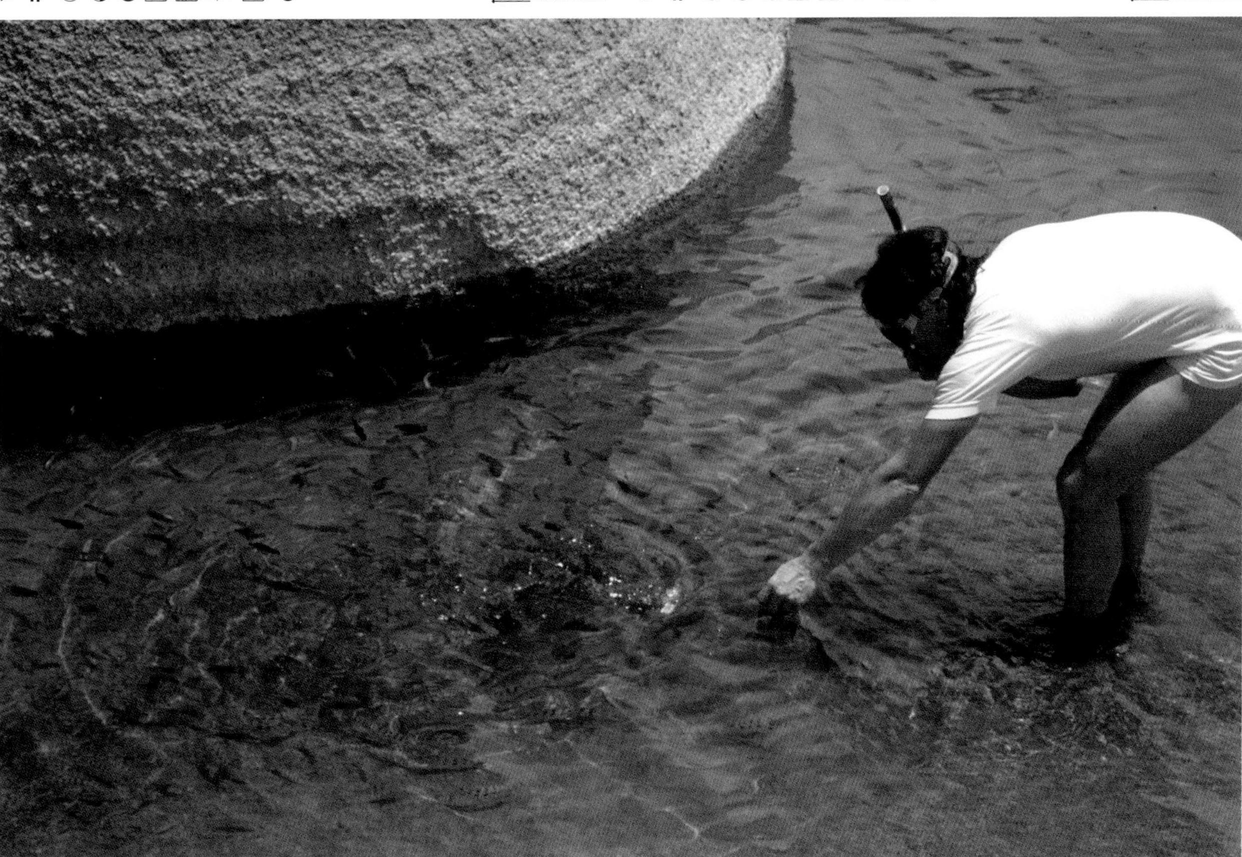

Der Malawisee - ein sehr großes Aquarium. Malawicichliden füttern bei Otter Point
Lake Malawi - a very big aquarium. Cichlid feeding at OtterPoint.

photo: E. Klaban

A05875-4 *Aulonocara* sp. "Jalo"

Lake Malawi: Jalo Reef, W,

photo: Ad Konings

A05875-4 *Aulonocara* sp. "Jalo"

Lake Malawi: Jalo Reef, W,

photo: Ad Konings

A05925-4 *Aulonocara* sp. "Stuartgranti Maleri"

Lake Malawi: Maleri Isl., W, 13 cm

♂

photo: J. Steves

A05925-4 *Aulonocara* sp. "Stuartgranti Maleri"

Lake Malawi: Maleri Isl., W, 13 cm

♀

photo: J. Steves

A05925-4 *Aulonocara* sp. "Stuartgranti Maleri"

Lake Malawi: Maleri Isl., W, 13 cm

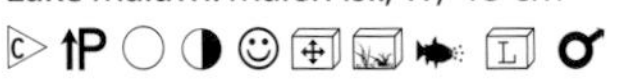

photo: B. Migge / Archiv A.C.S.

A05925-4 *Aulonocara* sp. "Stuartgranti Maleri"

Lake Malawi: Maleri Isl., W, 13 cm

photo: E. Schraml

A05926-5 *Aulonocara* sp. "Stuartgranti Maleri"
"Chipokae Red"
Z/X?, 13 cm

photo: E. Schraml

A05926-4 *Aulonocara* sp. "Stuartgranti Maleri"
"Chipokae Red"
Z/X?, 13 cm

photo: E. Schraml

A05918-4 *Aulonocara* sp. "Stuartgranti Maleri"
"Red Flash"
Z/X?, 13 cm

♂

photo: Ch. Wyrwich

A05918-4 *Aulonocara* sp. "Stuartgranti Maleri"
"Red Flash" (= "Baenschi Orange")
Z/X?, 13 cm
♂ **photo:** E. Schraml

A05918-4 *Aulonocara* sp. "Stuartgranti Maleri"
"Red Flash"
Z/X?, 13 cm
♀ **photo:** E. Schraml

A05918-5 *Aulonocara* sp. "Stuartgranti Maleri"
"Red Flash"
Z/X?, 13 cm
♂ **photo:** Piednoir

A05918-4 *Aulonocara* sp. "Stuartgranti Maleri"
"Red Flash"
Z/X?, 13 cm
♂ **photo:** Nakano/A.C.S.

A05927-4 *Aulonocara* sp. "Stuartgranti Maleri"
"Gelbbauch"
Z/X?, 13 cm
♂ **photo:** E. Schraml

A05928-4 *Aulonocara* sp. "Stuartgranti Maleri"

Lake Malawi: Chipoka, W, 11 cm
♂ **photo:** A. Spreinat

A05929-4 *Aulonocara* sp. "Stuartgranti Maleri"

Lake Malawi: Nakantenga Isl., W, 11 cm
♂ **photo:** Ad Konings

A05930-4 *Aulonocara* sp. "Stuartgranti Maleri"

Lake Malawi: Nankoma Isl., W, 11 cm
♂ **photo:** Ad Konings

A05931-5 *Aulonocara* sp. "Stuartgranti Maleri"

Lake Malawi: Chidunga Rocks, W, 11 cm

photo: Ad Konings

A05932-4 *Aulonocara* sp. "Stuartgranti Maleri"

Lake Malawi: Namalenje Isl., W, 11 cm

photo: Ad Konings

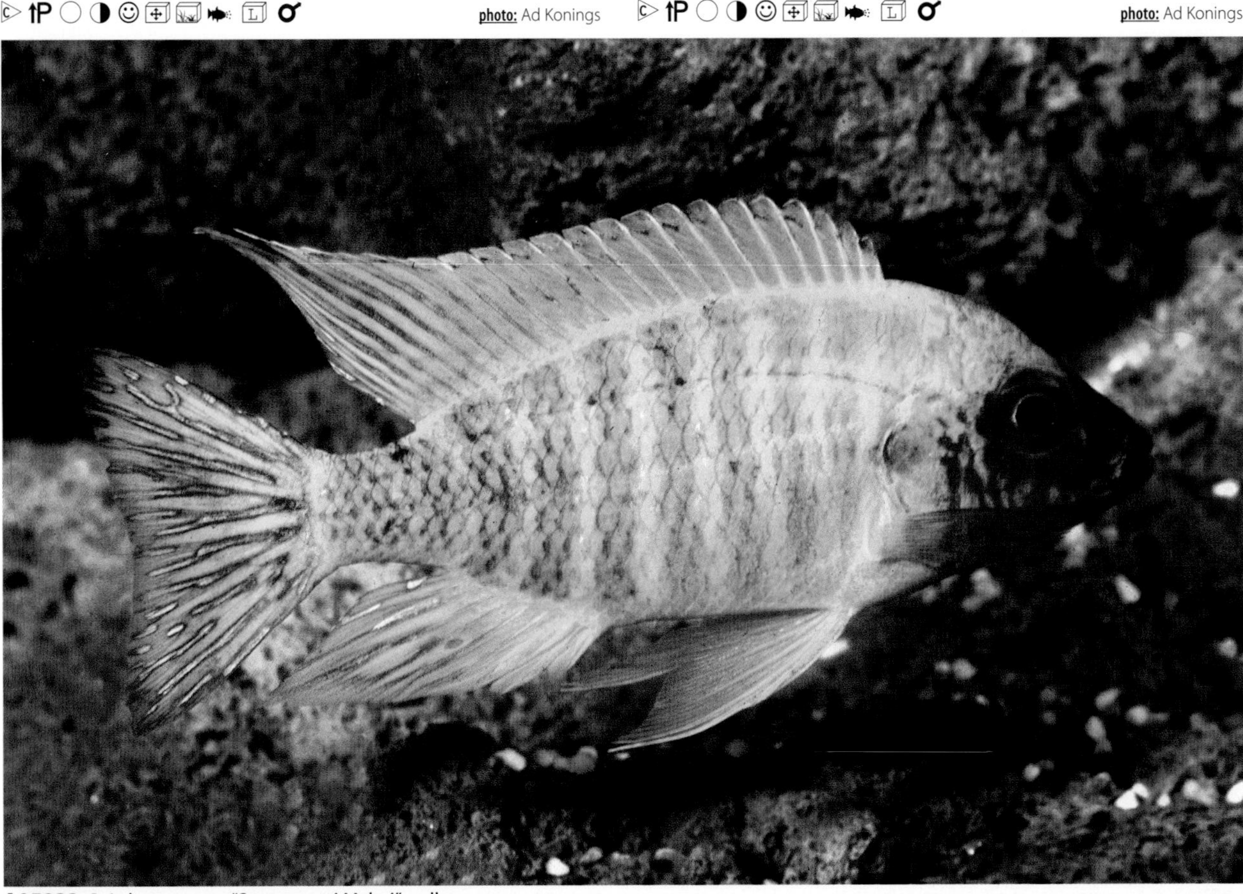

A05933-4 *Aulonocara* sp. "Stuartgranti Maleri", yellow

Lake Malawi: Maleri Isl., W, 11 cm

photo: Ad Konings

A05933-4 *Aulonocara* sp. "Stuartgranti Maleri", yellow

Lake Malawi: Maleri Isl., W, 11 cm

photo: Ch. Wyrwich

A05787-4 *Aulonocara baenschi* Meyer & Riehl, 1985

Lake Malawi: Benga, Nkhomo Reef, W, 10 cm

photo: W. van der Elst

A05787-4 *Aulonocara baenschi* MEYER & RIEHL, 1985

Lake Malawi: Benga, Nkhomo Reef, W, 10 cm

photo: E. Schraml

A05787-4 *Aulonocara baenschi* MEYER & RIEHL, 1985

Lake Malawi: Benga, Nkhomo Reef, W, 10 cm

photo: A. Spreinat

A05787-4 *Aulonocara baenschi* MEYER & RIEHL, 1985

Lake Malawi: Benga, Nkhomo Reef, W, 10 cm

photo: A. Spreinat

A05787-3 *Aulonocara baenschi* MEYER & RIEHL, 1985

Lake Malawi: Benga, Nkhomo Reef, W, 10 cm

photo: A. Spreinat

A05787-4 *Aulonocara baenschi* MEYER & RIEHL, 1985

Lake Malawi: Benga, Nkhomo Reef, W, 10 cm

photo: W. van der Elst

A05800-4 *Aulonocara korneliae* Meyer, Riehl & Zetzsche, 1987

Lake Malawi: Chisumulu Isl., W, 9 cm

♂

photo: H. J. Mayland

A05800-5 *Aulonocara korneliae* Meyer, Riehl & Zetzsche, 1987

Lake Malawi: Chisumulu Isl., W, 9 cm

♂

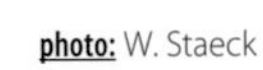

photo: W. Staeck

A05800-4 *Aulonocara korneliae* Meyer, Riehl & Zetzsche, 1987

Lake Malawi: Chisumulu Isl., W, 9 cm

♂

photo: E. Schraml

A05800-4 *Aulonocara korneliae* Meyer, Riehl & Zetzsche, 1987

Lake Malawi: Chisumulu Isl., W, 9 cm

♂

photo: E. Schraml

A05800-4 *Aulonocara korneliae* Meyer, Riehl & Zetzsche, 1987

Lake Malawi: Chisumulu Isl., W, 9 cm

♀

photo: E. Schraml

A05800-4 *Aulonocara korneliae* MEYER, RIEHL & ZETZSCHE, 1987

Lake Malawi: Chisumulu Isl., Chiteko, W, 9 cm

♂ **photo:** A. Spreinat

A05800-4 *Aulonocara korneliae* MEYER, RIEHL & ZETZSCHE, 1987

Lake Malawi: Chisumulu Isl., Chiteko, W, 9 cm

♀ **photo:** A. Spreinat

A05800-4 *Aulonocara korneliae* MEYER, RIEHL & ZETZSCHE, 1987

Lake Malawi: Chisumulu Isl., W, 9 cm

 **photo:** A. Spreinat

A05800-4 *Aulonocara korneliae* MEYER, RIEHL & ZETZSCHE, 1987

Lake Malawi: Chisumulu Isl., W, 9 cm

♀ **photo:** A. Spreinat

A05815-4 *Aulonocara hueseri* MEYER, RIEHL & ZETZSCHE, 1987

Lake Malawi: Mbuzi Isl., Likoma Isl., W, 9.5 cm

♂ ♀ **photo:** A. Spreinat

A05815-4 *Aulonocara hueseri* MEYER, RIEHL & ZETZSCHE, 1987

Lake Malawi: Likoma Isl., W, 9.5 cm

photo: E. Schraml

A05815-4 *Aulonocara hueseri* MEYER, RIEHL & ZETZSCHE, 1987

Lake Malawi: Likoma Isl., W, 9.5 cm

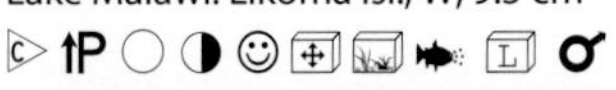

photo: A. Spreinat

A05815-4 *Aulonocara hueseri* MEYER, RIEHL & ZETZSCHE, 1987

Lake Malawi: Likoma Isl., W, 9.5 cm

photo: E. Schraml

A05815-4 *Aulonocara hueseri* MEYER, RIEHL & ZETZSCHE, 1987

Lake Malawi: Mbako Point, Likoma Isl., W, 9.5 cm

photo: A. Spreinat

A05815-5 *Aulonocara hueseri* MEYER, RIEHL & ZETZSCHE, 1987

Lake Malawi: Likoma Isl., W, 9.5 cm

photo: A. Spreinat

A05815-4 *Aulonocara hueseri* Meyer, Riehl & Zetzsche, 1987

Lake Malawi: Likoma Isl., W, 9.5 cm

photo: E. Schraml

A05815-4 *Aulonocara hueseri* Meyer, Riehl & Zetzsche, 1987

Lake Malawi: Likoma Isl., W, 9.5 cm

photo: E. Schraml

A05845-5 *Aulonocara maylandi* Trewavas, 1984

Lake Malawi: Eccles Reef, W, 12 cm

photo: H. J. Mayland

A05845-4 *Aulonocara maylandi* Trewavas, 1984

Lake Malawi: Eccles Reef, W, 12 cm

photo: E. Schraml

A05845-4 *Aulonocara maylandi* Trewavas, 1984

Lake Malawi: Eccles Reef, W, 12 cm

♂

photo: E. Schraml

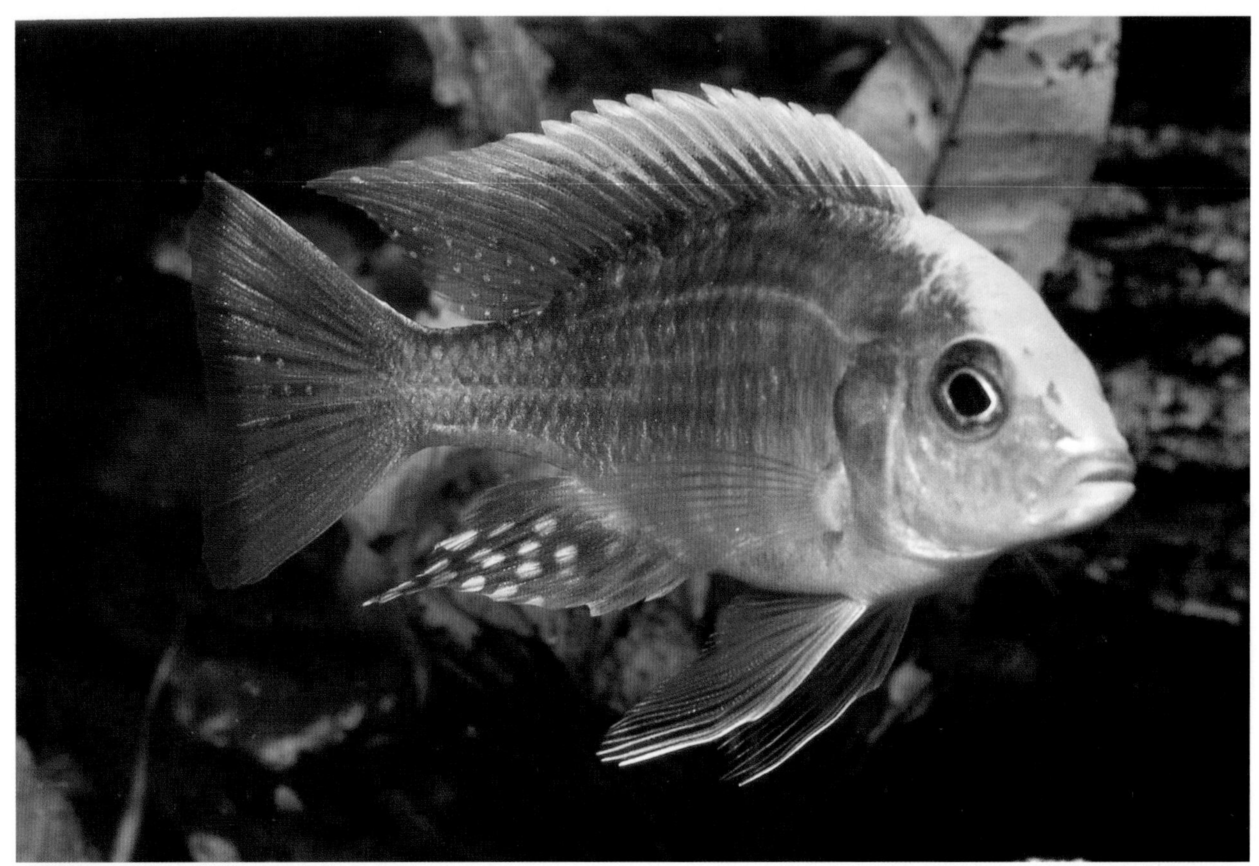

A05845-4 *Aulonocara maylandi* TREWAVAS, 1984

Lake Malawi: Eccles Reef, W, 12 cm

photo: H. J. Mayland

A05845-4 *Aulonocara maylandi* TREWAVAS, 1984

Lake Malawi: Eccles Reef, W, 12 cm

photo: H. J. Mayland

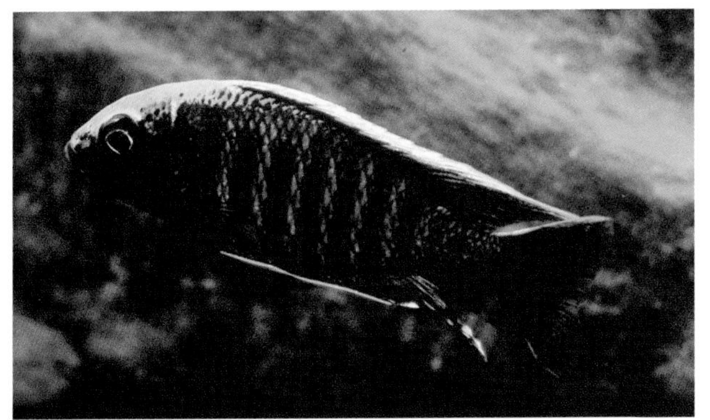

A05845-4 *Aulonocara maylandi* TREWAVAS, 1984

Lake Malawi: Eccles Reef, W, 12 cm

♂ **photo:** A. Spreinat

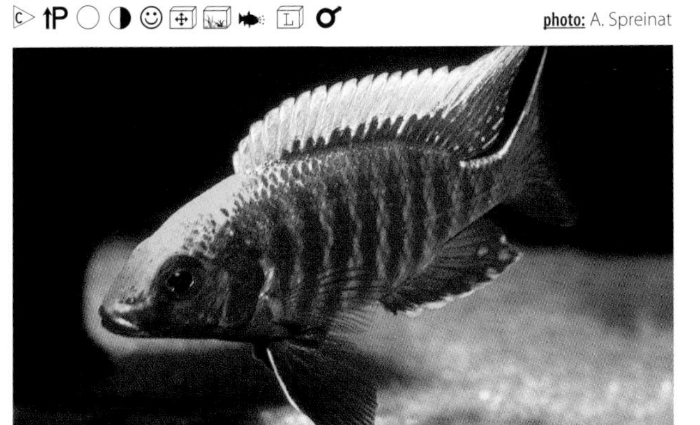

A05845-4 *Aulonocara maylandi* TREWAVAS, 1984

Lake Malawi: Eccles Reef, W, 12 cm

♂ **photo:** W. van der Elst

A05845-5 *Aulonocara maylandi* TREWAVAS, 1984

Lake Malawi: Eccles Reef, W, 12 cm

♂ **photo:** E. Schraml

A05845-5 *Aulonocara maylandi* TREWAVAS, 1984

Lake Malawi: Eccles Reef, W, 12 cm

♂ **photo:** W. van der Elst

A05845-4 *Aulonocara maylandi* TREWAVAS, 1984

Lake Malawi: Eccles Reef, W, 12 cm

♀ **photo:** A. Spreinat

A05845-4 *Aulonocara maylandi* TREWAVAS, 1984

Lake Malawi: Eccles Reef, W, 12 cm

♂ **photo:** E. Schraml

A05845-4 *Aulonocara maylandi* TREWAVAS, 1984

Lake Malawi: Eccles Reef, W, 12 cm

♂ **photo:** E. Schraml

A05845-4 *Aulonocara maylandi* TREWAVAS, 1984

Lake Malawi: Eccles Reef, W, 12 cm

♂ **photo:** A. Spreinat

Links / left: *Aulonocara maylandi*
Rechts / right: *Aulonocara kandeensis*

photo: H. J.Mayland

A05846-4 *Aulonocara kandeensis* TAWIL & ALLGAYER, 1987
Blue Orchid Aulonocara
Lake Malawi: Kande Isl., W, 11 cm
♂
photo: A. Spreinat

A05846-4 *Aulonocara kandeensis* TAWIL & ALLGAYER, 1987
Blue Orchid Aulonocara
Lake Malawi: Kande Isl., W, 11 cm
      ♂

photo: E. Schraml

A05846-4 *Aulonocara kandeensis* TAWIL & ALLGAYER, 1987
Blue Orchid Aulonocara
Lake Malawi: Kande Isl., W, 11 cm
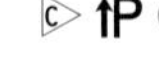     ♀
photo: E. Schraml

A05846-4 *Aulonocara kandeensis* TAWIL & ALLGAYER, 1987
Blue Orchid Aulonocara
Lake Malawi: Kande Isl., W, 11 cm
       ♂
photo: E. Schraml

A05846-4 *Aulonocara kandeensis* TAWIL & ALLGAYER, 1987
Blue Orchid Aulonocara
Lake Malawi: Kande Isl., W, 11 cm
    ♂
photo: Piednoir

A05802-5 *Aulonocara ethelwynnae* MEYER, RIEHL & ZETZSCHE, 1987
Chitendi Aulonocara
Lake Malawi: Chitendi Isl., W, 10 cm
♂

photo: Piednoir

A05802-4 *Aulonocara ethelwynnae* MEYER, RIEHL & ZETZSCHE, 1987
Chitendi Aulonocara
Lake Malawi: Chitendi Isl., W, 10 cm
♂

photo: A. Spreinat

A05802-4 *Aulonocara ethelwynnae* MEYER, RIEHL & ZETZSCHE, 1987
Chitendi Aulonocara
Lake Malawi: Chitendi Isl., W, 10 cm
♀

photo: A. Spreinat

A05802-4 *Aulonocara ethelwynnae* MEYER, RIEHL & ZETZSCHE, 1987
Chitendi Aulonocara
Lake Malawi: Chitendi Isl., W, 10 cm
♂

photo: A. Spreinat

A05802-4 *Aulonocara ethelwynnae* MEYER, RIEHL & ZETZSCHE, 1987
Chitendi Aulonocara
Lake Malawi: Chitendi Isl., W, 10 cm
♂

photo: A. Spreinat

A05795-4 *Aulonocara* sp. "Chitande Type Nkhomo"

Lake Malawi: Nkhomo Reef, W, 10 cm

♂

photo: Ad Konings

A05795-4 *Aulonocara* sp. "Chitande Type Nkhomo"

Lake Malawi: Nkhomo Reef, W, 10 cm

♀

photo: Ad Konings

A05842-4 *Aulonocara* sp. "Chitande Type North" fide Konings
= *A.* sp. "Black Top" fide Spreinat
Lake Malawi: Nkhata Bay, W, 10 cm
▷ ↑P ○ ◑ ☺ ⊞ ▭ ➧ Ⓛ ♂

photo: Ad Konings

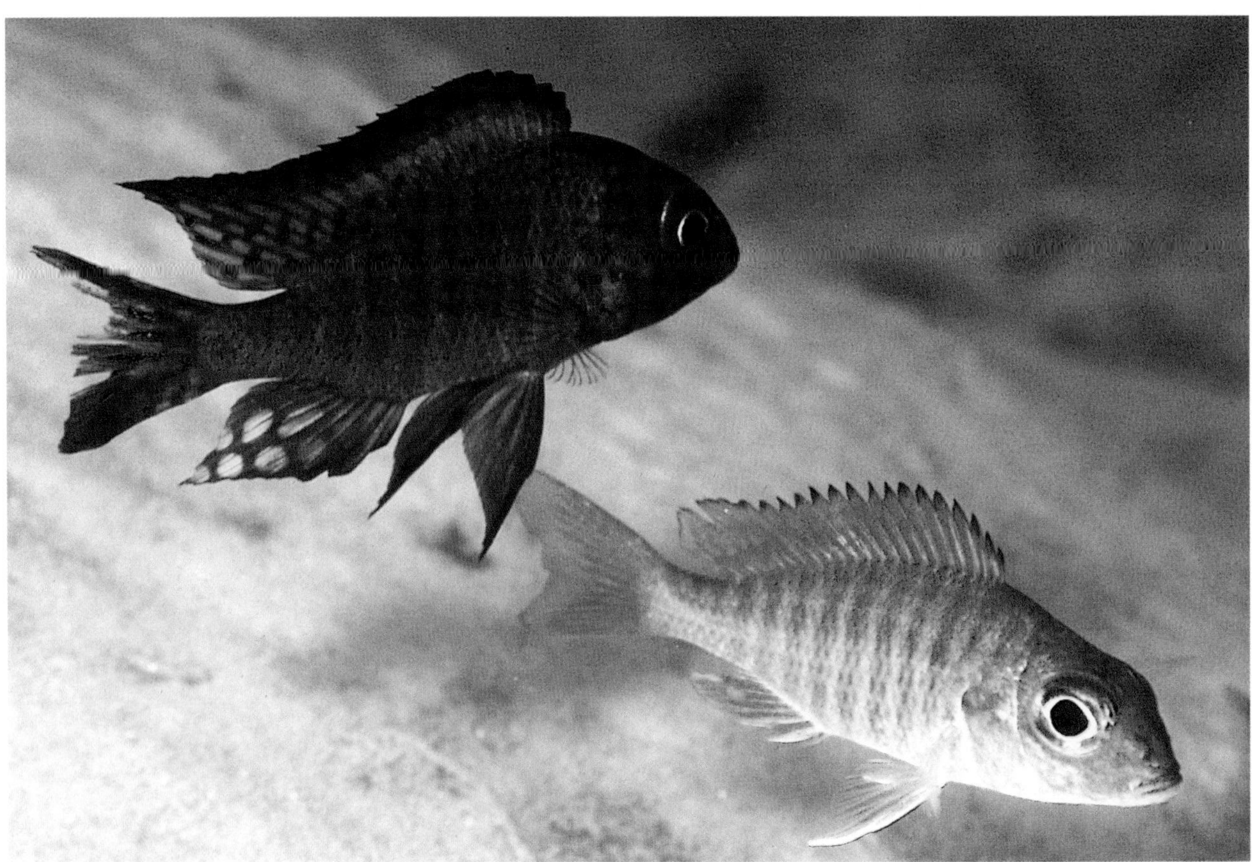

A05843-4 *Aulonocara* sp. "Chitande Type North" fide Konings
= *A.* sp. "Black Top" fide Spreinat
Lake Malawi: Mara Point (Moz.), W, 10 cm
▷ ↑P ○ ◑ ☺ ⊞ ▭ ➧ Ⓛ ♀ ♂

photo: Ad Konings

A05844-4 *Aulonocara* sp. "Chitande Type North" fide Konings
= *A.* sp. "Black Top" fide Spreinat
Lake Malawi: Hora Mhango, W, 10 cm
♂ photo: Ad Konings

A05847-4 *Aulonocara* sp. "Chitande Type North" fide Konings
= *A.* sp. "Black Top" fide Spreinat
Lake Malawi: Masimbwe Isl., Likoma, W, 10 cm
♂ photo: Ad Konings

A05847-4 *Aulonocara* sp. "Black Top" fide Spreinat
= *A.* sp. "Chitande Type North" fide Konings
Lake Malawi: Likoma: Masimbwe Isl., W, 10 cm
♂ photo: A. Spreinat

A05847-4 *Aulonocara* sp. "Black Top" fide Spreinat
= *A.* sp. "Chitande Type North" fide Konings
Lake Malawi: Likoma: Masimbwe Isl., W, 10 cm
♀ ♀ photo: A. Spreinat

A05848-4 *Aulonocara* sp. "Black Top" fide Spreinat
= *A.* sp. "Chitande Type North" fide Konings
Lake Malawi: Chisumulu Isl.: Chiteko, W, 10 cm
♂ photo: A. Spreinat

A05849-4 *Aulonocara* sp. "Black Top" fide Spreinat
= *A.* sp. "Chitande Type North" fide Konings
Lake Malawi: Cobue (Moz.): Namisi Rock, W, 10 cm
♂ photo: A. Spreinat

A05851-4 *Aulonocara* sp. "Kande Brown" fide Spreinat
= *A.* sp. "Chitande Type Kande" fide Konings
Lake Malawi: Kande Isl., W, 10 cm

♂ photo: A. Spreinat

A05851-4 *Aulonocara* sp. "Kande Brown" fide Spreinat
= *A.* sp. "Chitande Type Kande" fide Konings
Lake Malawi: Kande Isl., W, 10 cm
♀ photo: A. Spreinat

A05851-4 *Aulonocara* sp. "Chitande Type Kande" fide Konings
= *A.* sp. "Kande Brown" fide Spreinat
Lake Malawi: Kande Isl., W, 10 cm

photo: Ad Konings

A05851-3 *Aulonocara* sp. "Chitande Type Kande" fide Konings
= *A.* sp. "Kande Brown" fide Spreinat
Lake Malawi: Kande Isl., W, 10 cm

photo: H. J. Mayland

A05852-4 *Aulonocara* sp. "Chitendi Type East Coast"

Lake Malawi: Likoma, W, 10 cm

♂

photo: E. Schraml

A05852-4 *Aulonocara* sp. "Chitendi Type East Coast"

Lake Malawi: Likoma, W, 10 cm

♂

photo: E. Schraml

A05852-4 *Aulonocara* sp. "Chitendi Type East Coast"

Lake Malawi: Likoma, W, 10 cm

♀

photo: A. Spreinat

A05853-4 *Aulonocara* sp. "Chitendi Type East Coast"

Lake Malawi: Fort Maguire, Makanjila, W, 10 cm

photo: A. Spreinat

A05854-4 *Aulonocara* sp. "Chitendi Type East Coast"

Lake Malawi: Masinje, Makanjila, W, 10 cm

♂ ♀

photo: A. Spreinat

A05856-4 *Aulonocara* sp. "Chitendi Type East Coast"

Lake Malawi: Lupingu (Tan.), W, 10 cm

photo: A. Spreinat

A05857-4 *Aulonocara* sp. "Chitendi Type East Coast"

Lake Malawi: Lingwezi (Moz.), W, 10 cm

photo: A. Spreinat

A05860-4 *Aulonocara* sp. "Chitendi Type East Coast"
= *A.* sp. "Chitande Type Mozambique" fide Konings
Lake Malawi: Ponta Messuli (Moz.), W, 10 cm

photo: A. Spreinat

A05860-4 *Aulonocara* sp. "Chitendi Type East Coast"
= *A.* sp. "Chitande Type Mozambique" fide Konings
Lake Malawi: B, 10 cm

photo: Nakano/A.C.S.

A05881-4 *Aulonocara* sp. "Blue"

Lake Malawi: Ilala Gap and Domwe Isl., W, 10 cm

photo: P. Reinthal

A05882-4 *Aulonocara* sp. "Yellow Collar"

Lake Malawi: Otter Point, W, 10 cm

photo: P. Reinthal

A05883-4 *Aulonocara* sp. "Yellow Collar"

Lake Malawi: Tsano Rock, W, 10 cm

photo: Ad Konings

A05884-4 *Aulonocara* sp. "Blue Collar"
(= *A.* sp. "Yellow Collar" fide Konings)
Lake Malawi: Monkey Bay, W, 10 cm

photo: A.J. Ribbink

A05864-4 *Aulonocara* sp. "Chitande Type Mozambique"

Lake Malawi: Lumbaulo (Moz.), W, 10 cm

photo: Ad Konings

A05879-4 *Aulonocara* sp. "Chitande turquoise"

Lake Malawi: W, 10 cm

photo: African Trading AB

A05887-3 *Aulonocara* sp. "Yellow Top"
(= A. sp. "Lwanda")
Lake Malawi: Hai Reef (Tan.), W, 10-12 cm

photo: E. Schraml

A05887-4 *Aulonocara* sp. "Yellow Top"
(= A. sp. "Lwanda")
Lake Malawi: Hai Reef (Tan.), W, 10-12 cm

photo: E. Schraml

A05887-4 *Aulonocara* sp. "Yellow Top"
(= A. sp. "Lwanda")
Lake Malawi: Hai Reef (Tan.), W, 10-12 cm

photo: W. van der Elst

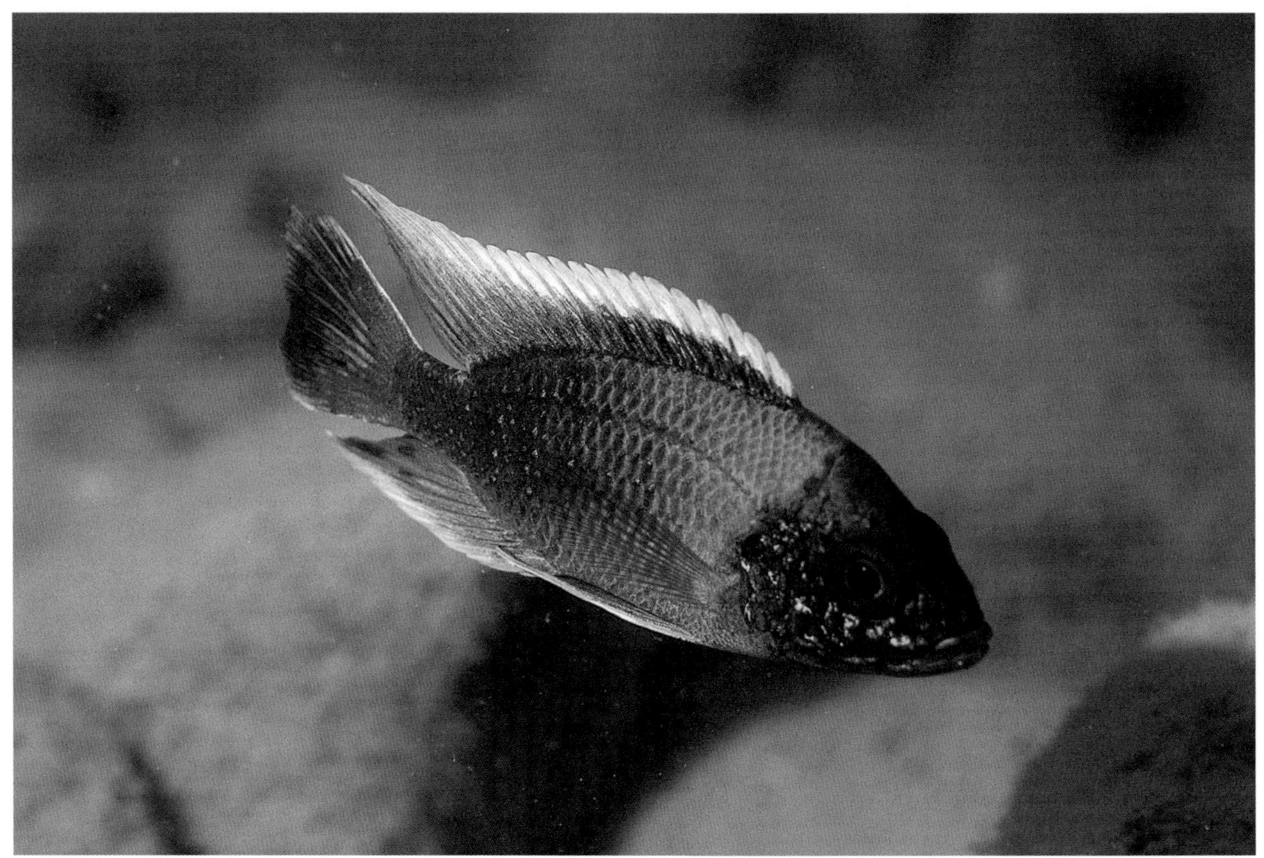

A05887-4 *Aulonocara* sp. "Yellow Top"
(= A. sp. "Lwanda")
Lake Malawi: Hai Reef (Tan.), W, 10-12 cm
♂

photo: A. Spreinat

A05887-4 *Aulonocara* sp. "Yellow Top"
(= A. sp. "Lwanda")
Lake Malawi: Hai Reef (Tan.), W, 10-12 cm
♀

photo: A. Spreinat

A05887-4 *Aulonocara* sp. "Yellow Top"
(= A. sp. "Lwanda")
Lake Malawi: Hai Reef (Tan.), W, 10-12 cm
♂
photo: A. Spreinat

A05888-3 *Aulonocara jacobfreibergi* (JOHNSON, 1974)
Albino-Zuchtform, juvenil
Z, 10-12 cm
photo: Nakano/A.C.S.

A05888-5 *Aulonocara jacobfreibergi* (JOHNSON, 1974)
Albino-Zuchtform
Z, 10-12 cm
♂
photo: Mal-Ta-Vi/E.S.

A05888-4 *Aulonocara jacobfreibergi* (JOHNSON, 1974)
Albino-Zuchtform
Z, 10-12 cm
♀
photo: Mal-Ta-Vi/E.S.

A05825-4 *Aulonocara jacobfreibergi* (JOHNSON, 1974)
Lake Malawi: B, 10-12 cm
♂
photo: Nakano/A.C.S.

A05889-4 *Aulonocara jacobfreibergi* (Johnson, 1974)

Lake Malawi: Otter Point, W, 10-12 cm

♂

photo: W. van der Elst

A05825-4 *Aulonocara jacobfreibergi* (Johnson, 1974)

Lake Malawi: B, 10-12 cm

photo: A. Spreinat

A05825-4 *Aulonocara jacobfreibergi* (Johnson, 1974)

Lake Malawi: B, 10-12 cm

photo: A. Spreinat

A05825-5 *Aulonocara jacobfreibergi* (Johnson, 1974)

Lake Malawi: B, 10-12 cm

♂

photo: E. Schraml

A05825-4 *Aulonocara jacobfreibergi* (Johnson, 1974)

Lake Malawi: W, 10-12 cm

♂

photo: W. Staeck

A05902-4 *Aulonocara jacobfreibergi* (JOHNSON, 1974)
"Orange Jacobfreibergi"
Lake Malawi: B, 10-12 cm

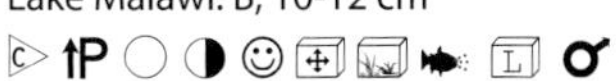

photo: A. Spreinat

A05902-5 *Aulonocara jacobfreibergi* (JOHNSON, 1974)
"Orange Jacobfreibergi"
Lake Malawi: B, 10-12 cm

photo: E. Schraml

A05902-4 *Aulonocara jacobfreibergi* (JOHNSON, 1974)
"Orange Jacobfreibergi"
Lake Malawi: B, 10-12 cm

photo: E. Schraml

A05825-4 *Aulonocara jacobfreibergi* (JOHNSON, 1974)

Lake Malawi: B, 10-12 cm

photo: E. Schraml

A05825-4 *Aulonocara jacobfreibergi* (JOHNSON, 1974)
"Regani"(?)
Lake Malawi: W, 10-12 cm

photo: E. Schraml

A96020-4 *Aulonocara jacobfreibergi* (JOHNSON, 1974)
"Reginae"
Lake Malawi: W, 10-12 cm

photo: W. van der Elst

A96020-4 *Aulonocara jacobfreibergi* (JOHNSON, 1974)
"Reginae"
Lake Malawi: W, 10-12 cm

photo: H. J. Mayland

A05901-4 *Aulonocara jacobfreibergi* (JOHNSON, 1974) "Eureka"
Lake Malawi: W, 10-12 cm
photo: E. Schraml

A05825-4 *Aulonocara jacobfreibergi* (JOHNSON, 1974)
Lake Malawi: B, 10-12 cm
photo: Nakano/A.C.S.

A05891-4 *Aulonocara jacobfreibergi* (JOHNSON, 1974)
Lake Malawi: Mbowe Isl., 10-12 cm

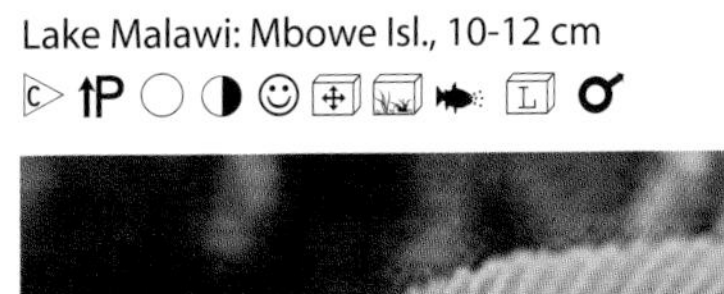

photo: Ad Konings

A05892-5 *Aulonocara jacobfreibergi* (JOHNSON, 1974)
Lake Malawi: around Cape Maclear, W, 10-12 cm
photo: E. Schraml

A05893-4 *Aulonocara jacobfreibergi* (JOHNSON, 1974)
Lake Malawi: Hongi Isl. (Tan.), W, 10-12 cm
photo: African Trading AB

A05820-4 *Aulonocara* sp. "Mamelela"

Lake Malawi: Undu Point (Tan.), W, 10 cm

photo: E. Schraml

A05820-5 *Aulonocara* sp. "Mamelela"

Lake Malawi: Undu Point (Tan.), W, 10 cm

photo: J. Steves

A05820-4 *Aulonocara* sp. "Mamelela"

Lake Malawi: Undu Point (Tan.), W, 10 cm

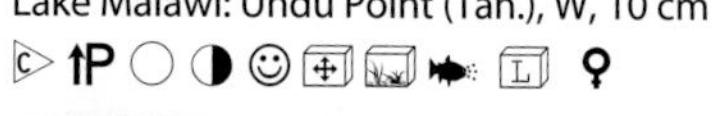

photo: E. Schraml

A05820-4 *Aulonocara* sp. "Mamelela"

Lake Malawi: Undu Point (Tan.), W, 10 cm

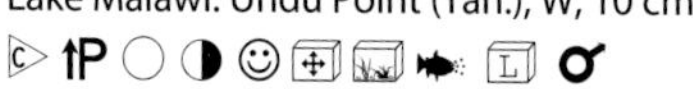

photo: A. Spreinat

A05910-4 *Aulonocara* sp. "Walteri"

Lake Malawi: Likoma Isl., Chizumulu Isl., B, 12-14 cm

photo: E. Schraml

A05910-4 *Aulonocara* sp. "Walteri"

Lake Malawi: Likoma Isl., Chizumulu Isl., B, 12-14 cm

photo: A. Spreinat

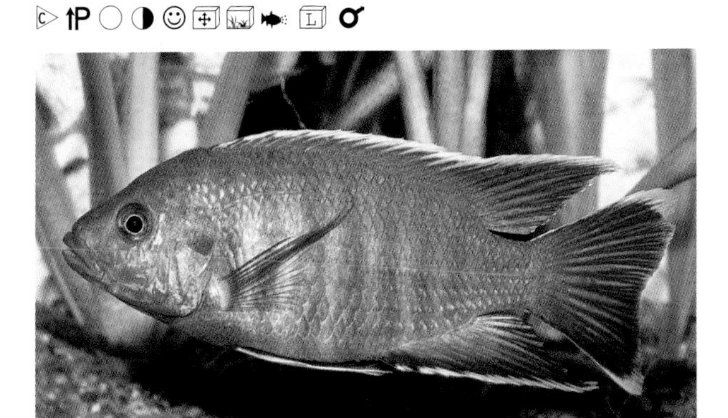

A05910-5 *Aulonocara* sp. "Walteri"

Lake Malawi: Likoma Isl., Chizumulu Isl., B, 12-14 cm

photo: A. Spreinat

A05910-5 *Aulonocara* sp. "Walteri"

Lake Malawi: Likoma Isl., Chizumulu Isl., B, 12-14 cm

photo: A. Spreinat

A05910-4 *Aulonocara* sp. "Walteri"

Lake Malawi: Likoma Isl., Chizumulu Isl., B, 12-14 cm

photo: A. Spreinat

A05910-4 *Aulonocara* sp. "Walteri"

Lake Malawi: Likoma Isl., Chizumulu Isl., W, 12-14 cm

photo: E. Schraml

A05948-4 *Aulonocara jacobfreiberg X Aulonocara baenschi*

B, X, 10 cm

photo: Piednoir

A05947-4 *Aulonocara jacobfreibergi X Astatotilapia calliptera*

B, X, 8 cm

photo: E. Schraml

A05991-5 *Aulonocara* "OB"
(= *A.* "Painted")
B, X, 10-12 cm

photo: W. Staeck

A05991-4 *Aulonocara* "OB"
(= *A.* "Painted")
B, X, 10-12 cm

photo: W. Staeck

A05991-4 *Aulonocara* "OB"
(= *A.* "Painted")
B, X, 10-12 cm

photo: W. Staeck

A05991-4 *Aulonocara* "OB"
(= *A.* "Painted")
B, X, 10-12 cm
photo: W. Staeck

A05991-4 *Aulonocara* "OB"
(= *A.* "Painted")
B, X, 10-12 cm
photo: W. Staeck

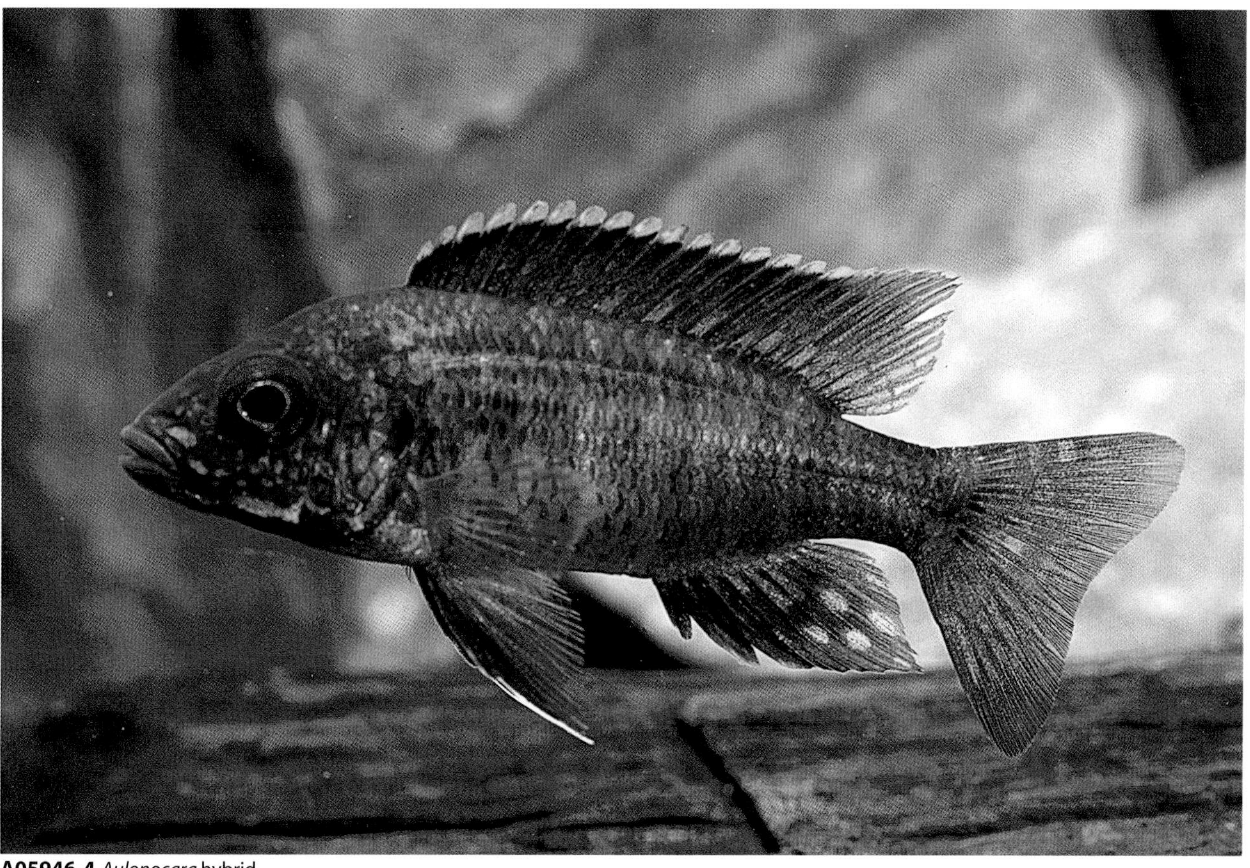

A05946-4 *Aulonocara* hybrid

B, X, 8-10 cm

photo: Nakano/A.C.S.

A05946-4 *Aulonocara* hybrid

B, X, 8-10 cm

photo: Piednoir

A05946-3 *Aulonocara* hybrid

B, X, 8-10 cm
photo: F. Teigler/A.C.S.

A05992-4 *Aulonocara* „Dragon Blood"

B, X, 8-10 cm

photo: S. Lehner

A05992-4 *Aulonocara* „Dragon Blood"

B, X, 8-10 cm

photo: S. Lehner

A05992-4 *Aulonocara* „Dragon Blood"

B, X, 8-10 cm

photo: S. Lehner

A05992-4 *Aulonocara* „Dragon Blood"

B, X, 8-10 cm

photo: S. Lehner

A05992-2 *Aulonocara* „Dragon Blood"

B, X, 8-10 cm

photo: S. Lehner

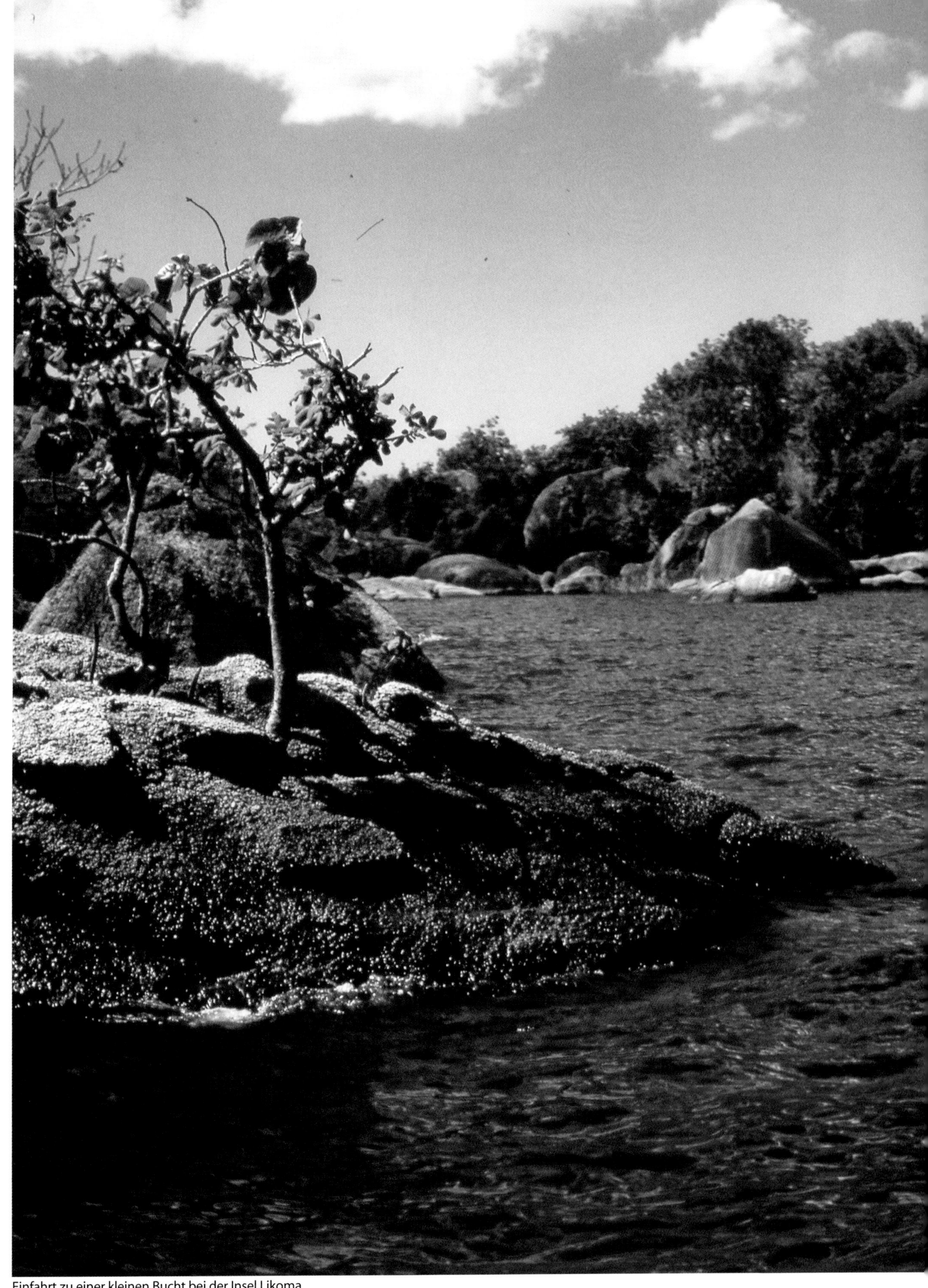
Einfahrt zu einer kleinen Bucht bei der Insel Likoma.
Entry to a small bay near Likoma island.

photo: H. J. Mayland

A41701-4 *Lethrinops lethrinus* (GÜNTHER, 1894)

Lake Malawi: Senga Bay; W, 20 cm.

photo: Ad Konings

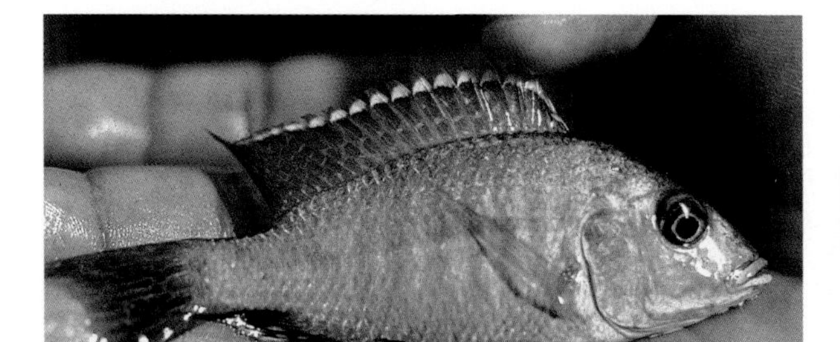

A41701-3 *Lethrinops lethrinus* (GÜNTHER, 1894)

Lake Malawi: Senga Bay; W, 20 cm.

photo: Ad Konings

A41702-4 *Lethrinops lethrinus* (GÜNTHER, 1894)

Lake Malawi: Thumbi Isl.; W, 20 cm.

photo: Ad Konings

A41703-4 *Lethrinops lethrinus* (GÜNTHER, 1894)
Lakes Malawi and Malombe, upper Shire River, small perennial rivers on the western shore of Lake Malawi; W, 20 cm.

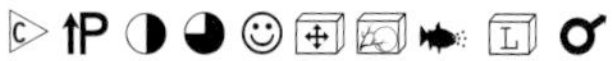

photo: Piednoir

A41703-4 *Lethrinops lethrinus* (GÜNTHER, 1894)
Lakes Malawi and Malombe, upper Shire River, small perennial rivers on the western shore of Lake Malawi; W, 20 cm.

photo: A. Spreinat

A41704-4 *Lethrinops* sp. "Mbasi"

Lake Malawi; W, 18 cm.

photo: Mal-Ta-Vi/E.S.

A41704-4 *Lethrinops* sp. "Mbasi"

Lake Malawi; W, 18 cm.

♀

photo: Mal-Ta-Vi/E.S.

A41705-4 *Lethrinops* sp. "Red Capuz"

Lake Malawi; W, 14 cm

photo: Mal-Ta-Vi/E.S.

A41705-4 *Lethrinops* sp. "Red Capuz"

Lake Malawi; W, 14 cm

photo: Mal-Ta-Vi/E.S.

A41705-4 *Lethrinops* sp. "Red Capuz"

Lake Malawi; W, 14 cm

photo: Mal-Ta-Vi/E.S.

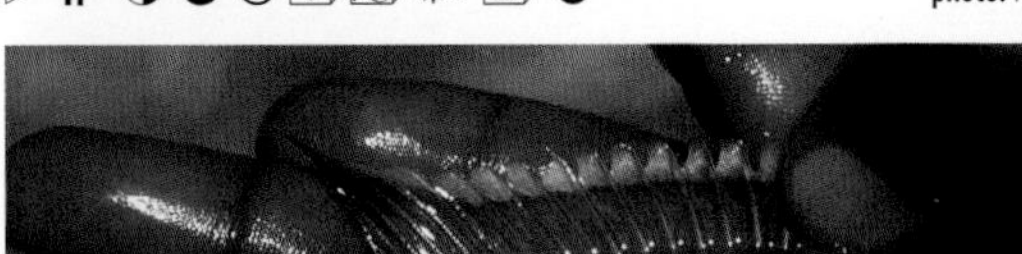

A41706-4 *Lethrinops* sp. "Small Green Face"

Lake Malawi: Senga Bay; W, ? cm

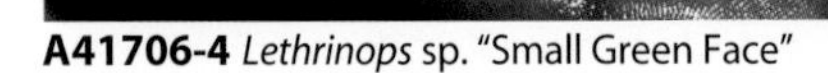

photo: M. Smith

A41707-4 *Lethrinops albus* Regan, 1922

Lake Malawi: Kande Isl.; W, 15 cm

photo: Ad Konings

A41708-3 *Lethrinops* cf. *albus* REGAN, 1922 [fide KONINGS, 2001]
= *Lethrinops* cf. *marginatus* AHL, 1927 [fide KONINGS, 1995]
Lake Malawi: Senga Bay; W, 13 cm

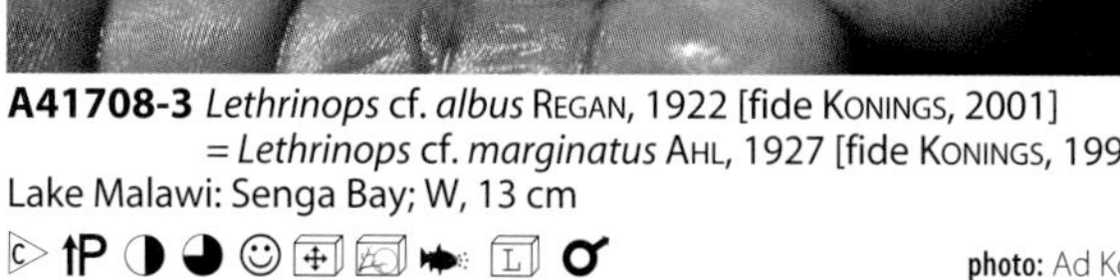

♂ **photo:** Ad Konings

A41708-3 *Lethrinops* cf. *albus* REGAN, 1922 [fide KONINGS, 2001]
= *Lethrinops* cf. *marginatus* AHL, 1927 [fide KONINGS, 1995]
Lake Malawi: Senga Bay; W, 13 cm

♀ **photo:** Ad Konings

A41709-3 *Lethrinops/Tramitichromis* sp. I

Lake Malawi: Katoto Beach/Nkhata Bay; W, 8 cm

♂ **photo:** A. Spreinat

A41709-3 *Lethrinops/Tramitichromis* sp. I

Lake Malawi: Katoto Beach/Nkhata Bay; W, 8 cm

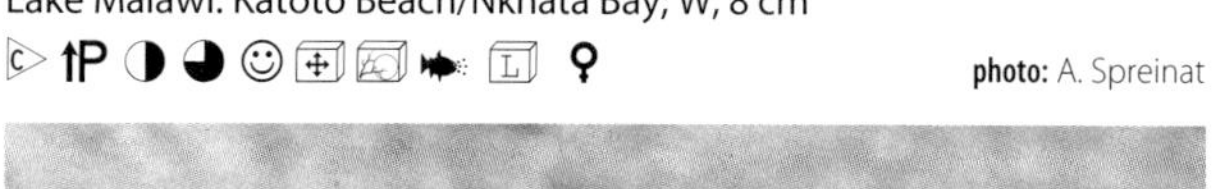

♀ **photo:** A. Spreinat

A41710-4 *Lethrinops/Tramitichromis* sp. II

Lake Malawi, W, 15 cm

♂ **photo:** W. Staeck

A41710-4 *Lethrinops/Tramitichromis* sp. II

Lake Malawi, W, ? cm

♀ **photo:** W. Staeck

A41711-4 *Lethrinops* cf. *furcifer* TREWAVAS, 1931

Lake Malawi: Mphande/Metangula/Moz.; W, 20 cm

♂ **photo:** A. Spreinat

A41712-4 *Lethrinops* cf. *furcifer* TREWAVAS, 1931

Lake Malawi: Lupono/Mbamba Bay; W, 20 cm

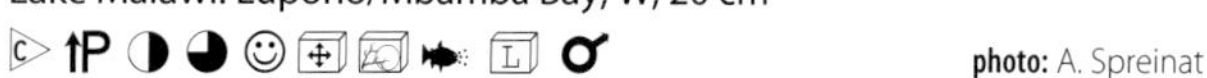

♂ **photo:** A. Spreinat

A41713-4 *Lethrinops* sp. "Black Fin Lupingu"

Lake Malawi: Lupingu; W, 15 cm

photo: Mal-Ta-Vi/E.S.

A41713-4 *Lethrinops* sp. "Black Fin Lupingu"

Lake Malawi: Lupingu; W, 15 cm

photo: Mal-Ta-Vi/E.S.

A41714-4 *Lethrinops* sp. "Double Blotch"

Lake Malawi; W, ? cm

♂

photo: A. Spreinat

A41714-4 *Lethrinops* sp. "Double Blotch"

Lake Malawi; W, ? cm

♀

photo: A. Spreinat

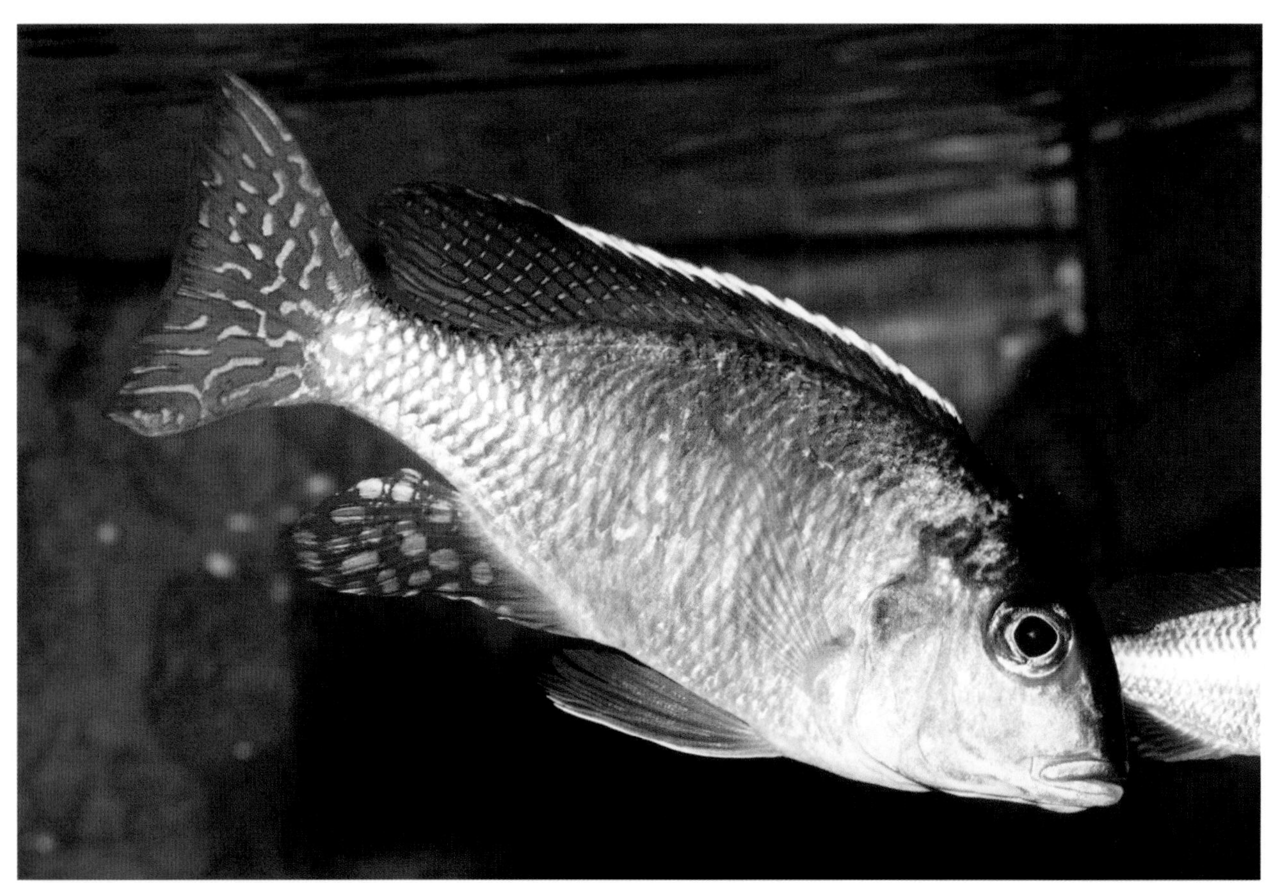

A41715-4 *Lethrinops* sp. "Red Shoulder"

Lake Malawi: Senga Bay; W, 20 cm

♂

photo: A. Spreinat

A41715-4 *Lethrinops* sp. "Red Shoulder"

Lake Malawi: Senga Bay; W, 20 cm

♀

photo: A. Spreinat

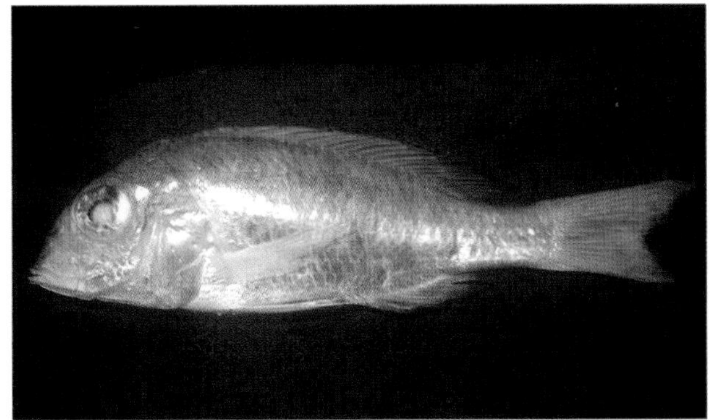

A41716-3 *Lethrinops marginatus* AHL, 1927
BMNH 1930.1.31.163 (stored as *L. oculatus* TREWAVAS, 1931)
Lake Malawi; 13 cm
photo: E.Schraml

A41716-4 *Lethrinops marginatus* AHL, 1927
(= *L. oculatus* TREWAVAS, 1931), see also pp. 85 and 110
Lake Malawi: Senga Bay; W, 18 cm
♂ **photo:** Ad Konings

A41716-4 *Lethrinops marginatus* AHL, 1927
(= *L. oculatus* TREWAVAS, 1931), see also pp. 85 and 110
Lake Malawi: Senga Bay; W, 18 cm
♂ **photo:** Ad Konings

A41717-3 *Lethrinops* cf. *marginatus* AHL, 1927
see also pp. 85 and 110
Lake Malawi; W, ? cm
♀ **photo:** W. Staeck

A41718-5 *Lethrinops furcifer* TREWAVAS, 1931

Lake Malawi: Chitande, W, 19 cm
♂ **photo:** Ad Konings

A41720-4 *Lethrinops furcifer* Trewavas, 1931

Lake Malawi: Senga Bay, W, 19 cm

♂ photo: Ad Konings

A41720-4 *Lethrinops furcifer* Trewavas, 1931

Lake Malawi: Senga Bay, W, 19 cm

♀ photo: Ad Konings

A41719-5 *Lethrinops* cf. *furcifer* Trewavas, 1931

Lake Malawi: Chitande, W, 19 cm

♂ photo: M.Smith

A41721-4 *Lethrinops* sp. "Mdoka Red"

Lake Malawi: Mdoka, W, ? cm

♂ photo: Ad Konings

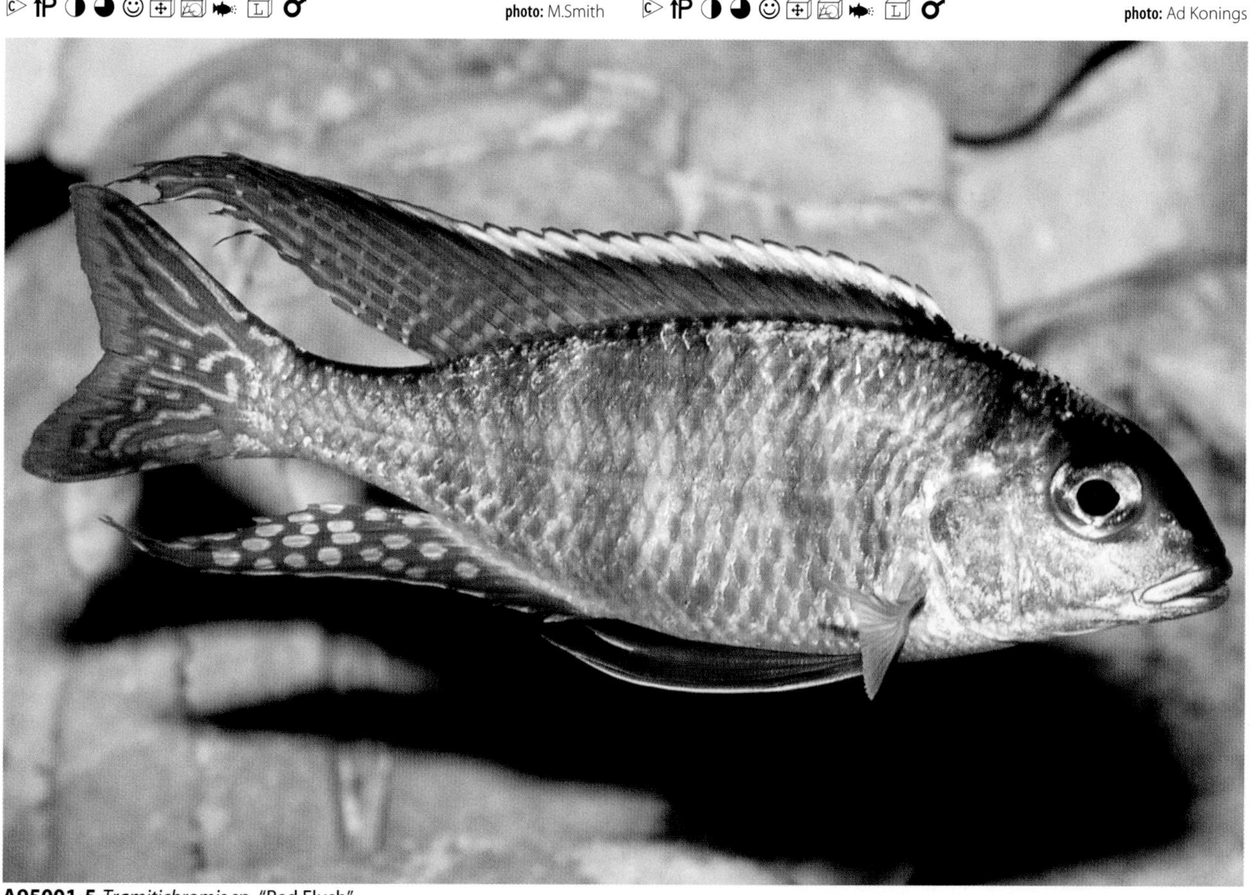

A95001-5 *Tramitichromis* sp. "Red Flush"
(=? *T. variabilis* (Trewavas, 1931))
Lake Malawi: Senga Bay; W, 15 cm

♂ photo: H. J. Mayland

A95001-4 *Tramitichromis* sp. "Red Flush"
(=? *T. variabilis* (TREWAVAS, 1931))
Lake Malawi: Senga Bay; W, 15 cm

photo: E. Schraml

A95001-4 *Tramitichromis* sp. "Red Flush"
(=? *T. variabilis* (TREWAVAS, 1931))
Lake Malawi: Senga Bay; W, 15 cm

photo: W. van der Elst

A95001-3 *Tramitichromis* sp. "Red Flush"
(=? *T. variabilis* (TREWAVAS, 1931))
Lake Malawi: Senga Bay; W, 15 cm

photo: M. Smith

A95001-3 *Tramitichromis* sp. "Red Flush"
(=? *T. variabilis* (TREWAVAS, 1931))
Lake Malawi: Senga Bay; W, 15 cm

photo: E. Schraml

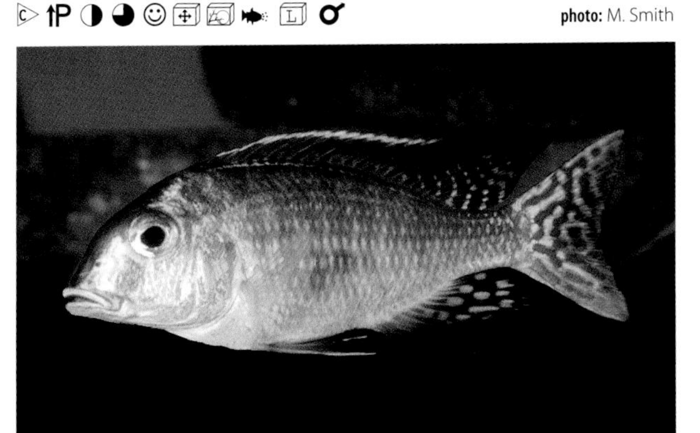

A95001-3 *Tramitichromis* sp. "Red Flush"
(=? *T. variabilis* (TREWAVAS, 1931))
Lake Malawi: Senga Bay; W, 15 cm

photo: E. Schraml

A95001-3 *Tramitichromis* sp. "Red Flush"
(=? *T. variabilis* (TREWAVAS, 1931))
Lake Malawi: Senga Bay; W, 15 cm

photo: E. Schraml

A95000-4 *Tramitichromis variabilis* (TREWAVAS, 1931)

Lake Malawi: Likoma Isl.; 17 cm

photo: Ad Konings

A95002-4 *Tramitichromis* cf. *variabilis* (TREWAVAS, 1931)

Lake Malawi: Nkhata Bay; 17 cm

photo: Mark Smith

A95003-4 *Tramitichromis brevis* (Boulenger, 1908)

Lake Malawi: Mbungu/Likoma Isl.; W, 16 cm

♂

photo: A. Spreinat

A95004-4 *Tramitichromis brevis* (Boulenger, 1908)

Lake Malawi: Likula/Chisumulu; W, 16 cm

♀

photo: A. Spreinat

A95004-4 *Tramitichromis brevis* (BOULENGER, 1908)

Lake Malawi: Likula/Chisumulu; W, 16 cm

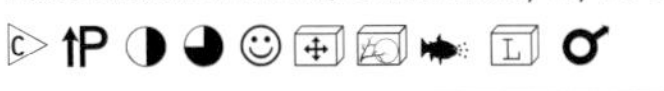

photo: A. Spreinat

A95005-4 *Tramitichromis brevis* (BOULENGER, 1908)

Lake Malawi: Nkhata Bay; 16 cm

photo: A. Spreinat

A95006-4 *Tramitichromis intermedius* (TREWAVAS, 1935)

Lake Malawi; W, 16 cm

photo: Mal-Ta-Vi/E.S.

A95006-4 *Tramitichromis intermedius* (TREWAVAS, 1935)

Lake Malawi; W, 16 cm

photo: M. Smith

A95006-4 *Tramitichromis intermedius* (TREWAVAS, 1935)

Lake Malawi; W, 16 cm

♀

photo: Mal-Ta-Vi/E.S.

A95007-4 *Tramitichromis trilineata* (TREWAVAS, 1931)

Lake Malawi: Chembe; W, 14 cm

♀ **photo:** Ad Konings

A95011-4 *Tramitichromis lituris* (TREWAVAS, 1931) [fide TURNER, 1996]
Tramitichromis sp. "Lituris Yellow" (fide KONINGS)
Lake Malawi: S-E-Arm; W, 17 cm

♂ **photo:** G. Turner

A95008-4 *Tramitichromis* cf. *lituris* (TREWAVAS, 1931)

Lake Malawi: W, 17 cm

♂ **photo:** Mal-Ta-Vi/E.S.

A95008-4 *Tramitichromis* cf. *lituris* (TREWAVAS, 1931)

Lake Malawi: W, 17 cm

♀ **photo:** Mal-Ta-Vi/E.S.

A95009-4 *Tramitichromis lituris* (TREWAVAS, 1931)

Lake Malawi: W, 17 cm

♂ **photo:** Mal-Ta-Vi/E.S.

A95009-4 *Tramitichromis lituris* (TREWAVAS, 1931)

Lake Malawi: W, 17 cm

♀ **photo:** Mal-Ta-Vi/E.S.

A95010-4 *Tramitichromis lituris* (TREWAVAS, 1931)
= *Tramitichromis* sp. "Orange"
Lake Malawi: W, 17 cm

♂ **photo:** Mal-Ta-Vi/E.S.

A95010-4 *Tramitichromis lituris* (TREWAVAS, 1931)
= *Tramitichromis* sp. "Orange"
Lake Malawi: W, 17 cm

♀ **photo:** Mal-Ta-Vi/E.S.

A95008-3 *Tramitichromis* cf. *lituris* (Trewavas, 1931)

Lake Malawi: W, 17 cm

♂

photo: Mal-Ta-Vi/E.S.

A95008-3 *Tramitichromis* cf. *lituris* (Trewavas, 1931)

Lake Malawi: W, 17 cm

♀

photo: Mal-Ta-Vi/E.S.

A41722-5 *Lethrinops* sp.

Lake Malawi: Senga Bay; W, 20 cm

photo: M.Smith

A41723-4 *Lethrinops lunaris* TREWAVAS, 1931

Lake Malawi: Senga Bay; W, 18.6 cm

photo: Ad Konings

A41723-4 *Lethrinops lunaris* TREWAVAS, 1931

Lake Malawi: Senga Bay; W, 18.6 cm

photo: Ad Konings

A41723-4 *Lethrinops lunaris* TREWAVAS, 1931
preserved specimen: syntype BMNH 1921.9.6.208 [21105]
Lake Malawi: Senga Bay; 18.6 cm

photo: E. Schraml

A41724-4 *Lethrinops* sp. "Longipinnis Orange Head"

Lake Malawi: Domira Bay; W, 21 cm

photo: G. Turner

A41725-4 *Lethrinops longipinnis* ECCLES & LEWIS, 1978
preserved specimen: BMNH 1977.5.24.8.10 [21009]
Lake Malawi; W, 19 cm

photo: E. Schraml

A41726-5 *Lethrinops* sp. "Christyi Fort Maguire"

Lake Malawi: Fort Magure; W, 20 cm

photo: M. Smith

A41727-5 *Lethrinops* sp. "Lumbira Deep"
(=? *Lethrinops longipinnis* ECCLES & LEWIS, 1978)
Lake Malawi: Lumbira/Tansania; W, 19 cm

photo: A. Spreinat

A41725-5 *Lethrinops longipinnis* Eccles & Lewis, 1978

Lake Malawi: S-E-Arm; W, 19 cm

photo: G. Turner

A41728-5 *Lethrinops* sp. "Longipinnis Ntekete"

Lake Malawi: Ntekete/Makanjila; W, 19 cm

photo: A. Spreinat

A41728-5 *Lethrinops* sp. "Longipinnis Ntekete"

Lake Malawi: Ntekete/Makanjila; W, 19 cm

photo: Ad Konings

A41728-5 *Lethrinops* sp. "Longipinnis Ntekete"

Lake Malawi: Ntekete/Makanjila; W, 19 cm

photo: Ad Konings

A41729-4 *Lethrinops gossei* Burgess & Axelrod, 1973

Lake Malawi: Masinje/Fort Maguire; W, 17 cm

photo: M. Smith

A41730-5 *Lethrinops* sp. "Mbenji Deep"

Lake Malawi: Mbenji Isl.; W, 15 cm

♂ photo: M. Smith

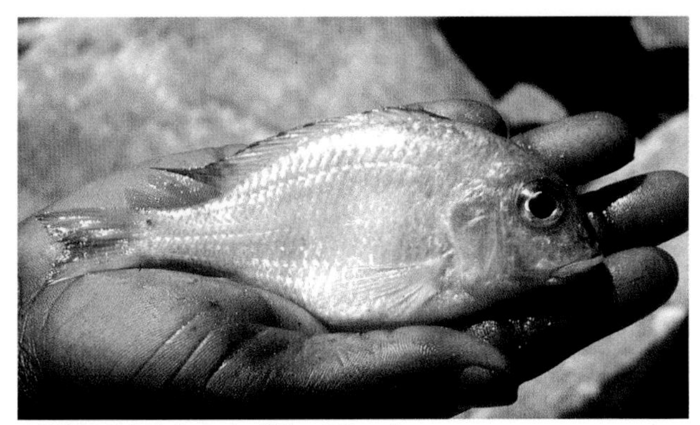

A41730-5 *Lethrinops* sp. "Mbenji Deep"

Lake Malawi: Mbenji Isl.; W, 15 cm

♀ photo: M. Smith

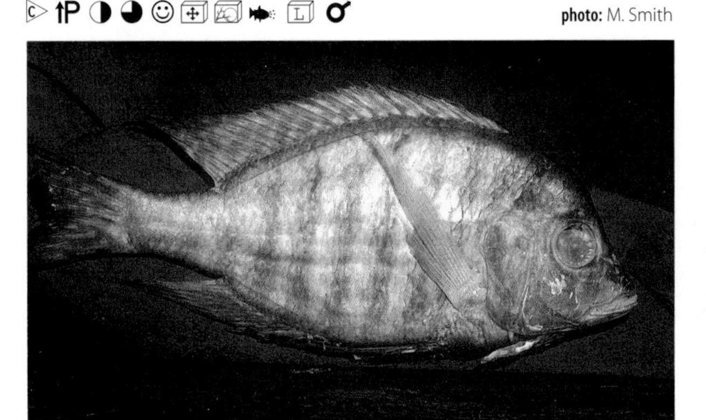

A41731-5 *Lethrinops macracanthus* TREWAVAS, 1931
preserved specimen: BMNH 1969.3.11.26
Lake Malawi; W, 20 cm

photo: E. Schraml

A41732-4 *Lethrinops longimanus* TREWAVAS, 1931
preserved specimen: BMNH [21005]
Lake Malawi; W, 18 cm

photo: E. Schraml

A41732-4 *Lethrinops longimanus* TREWAVAS, 1931

Lake Malawi: Domira Bay; W, 18 cm

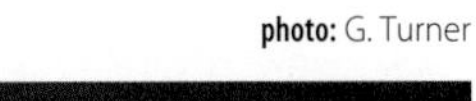

photo: G. Turner

A41733-4 *Lethrinops* sp. "Longimanus Likoma"

Lake Malawi: Namisi Rock/Cobue/Moz.; W, 10 cm

photo: A. Spreinat

A41734-4 *Lethrinops* sp. "Longimanus Likoma"

Lake Malawi: Mbako Bay; W, 10 cm

♂ photo: Ad Konings

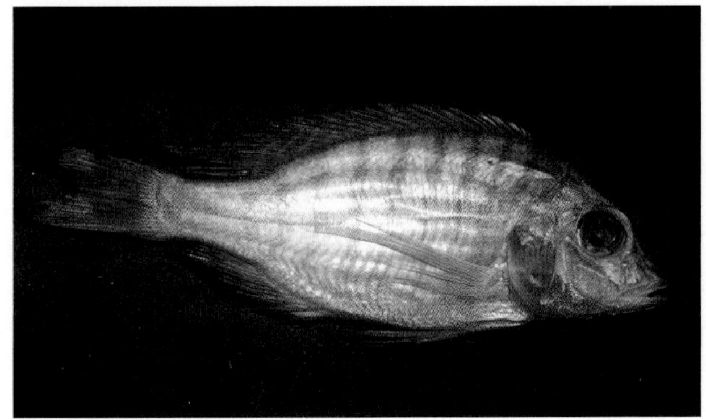

A41735-4 *Lethrinops parvidens* TREWAVAS, 1931
preserved specimen: BMNH 1978.10.31:34
Lake Malawi: Mazinzi Bay; 16 cm

photo: E. Schraml

A41736-4 *Lethrinops* sp. "Longimanus Likoma"

Lake Malawi: Mara Point; W, 10 cm

photo: Ad Konings

Chisumulu Island

photo: H. J. Mayland

A41737-4 *Lethrinops* sp. "Aulonocara Type"

Lake Malawi: coast of Tanzania; W, 17 cm

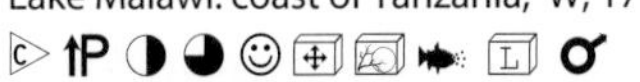

photo: Mal-Ta-Vi/E.S.

A41737-4 *Lethrinops* sp. "Aulonocara Type"

Lake Malawi: coast of Tanzania; W, 17 cm

photo: Mal-Ta-Vi/E.S.

A41738-4 *Lethrinops micrentodon* (REGAN, 1922)

Lake Malawi: Makokola; W, 11.5 cm

photo: Ad Konings

A41738-4 *Lethrinops micrentodon* (REGAN, 1922)

Lake Malawi: Makokola; W, 11.5 cm

photo: Ad Konings

A41738-3 *Lethrinops micrentodon* (REGAN, 1922)

Lake Malawi: Makokola; W, 11.5 cm

photo: A. Spreinat

A41738-4 *Lethrinops micrentodon* (REGAN, 1922)

Lake Malawi: Makokola; W, 11.5 cm

photo: A. Spreinat

A41738-3 *Lethrinops micrentodon* (REGAN, 1922)

Lake Malawi: Makokola; W, 11.5 cm

photo: A. Spreinat

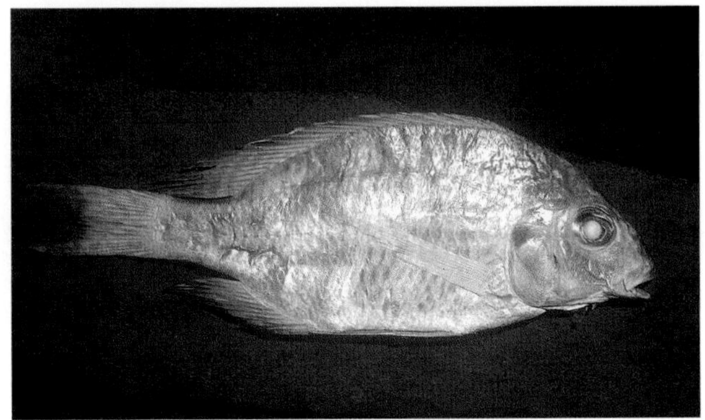

A41738-4 *Lethrinops micrentodon* (REGAN, 1922)
preserved specimen: BMNH 1935.6.14.2007
Lake Malawi; W, 11.5 cm

photo: E. Schraml

A41738-4 *Lethrinops* sp. "Micrentodon Makokola"
= *Lethrinops micrentodon* (REGAN, 1922)
Lake Malawi: Makokola; W, 13 cm

photo: G. Turner

A41739-4 *Lethrinops* sp. "Lowae"

Lake Malawi: S-E-Arm; W, 17 cm

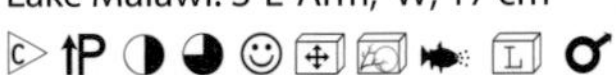

photo: G. Turner

A41740-4 *Lethrinops* sp. "Yellow Chin"

Lake Malawi: SE-Arm; W, 11 cm

photo: G. Turner

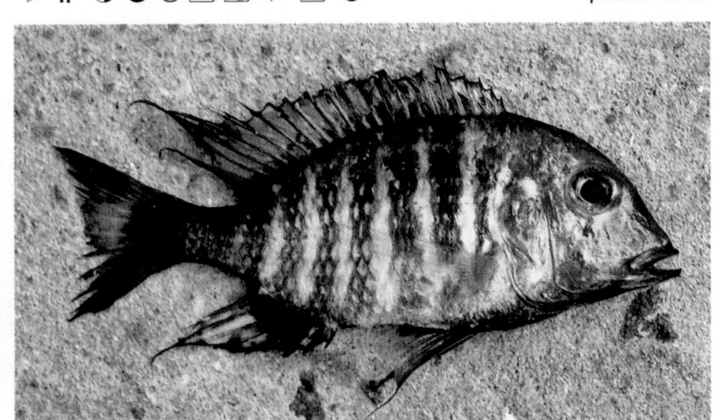

A41741-4 *Lethrinops* sp. "Deepwater Albus"

Lake Malawi: W, 15 cm

photo: G. Turner

A41742-3 *Lethrinops* sp. "Macrostoma"

Lake Malawi: Fowo; Namalaka; W, 11 cm

♀ **photo:** G. Turner

A41743-4 *Lethrinops* sp. "Oliveri"

Lake Malawi: SE-Arm; W, 15 cm

♂ **photo:** G. Turner

A41744-4 *Lethrinops mylodon* Eccles & Lewis, 1979

Lake Malawi: SE-Arm; W, 25 cm

♂ **photo:** G. Turner

A41744-3 *Lethrinops mylodon* Eccles & Lewis, 1979

Lake Malawi: Domira Bay; W, 25 cm

♂ **photo:** G. Turner

A41745-4 *Lethrinops microdon* Eccles & Trewavas, 1989

Lake Malawi: SE-Arm; W, 20 cm

♂ **photo:** G. Turner

A41745-4 *Lethrinops microdon* Eccles & Trewavas, 1989

Lake Malawi: SE-Arm; W, 20 cm

♀ **photo:** G. Turner

A41746-4 *Lethrinops* sp. "Dark"

Lake Malawi: S-E-Arm; W, 10 cm

♂ **photo:** G. Turner

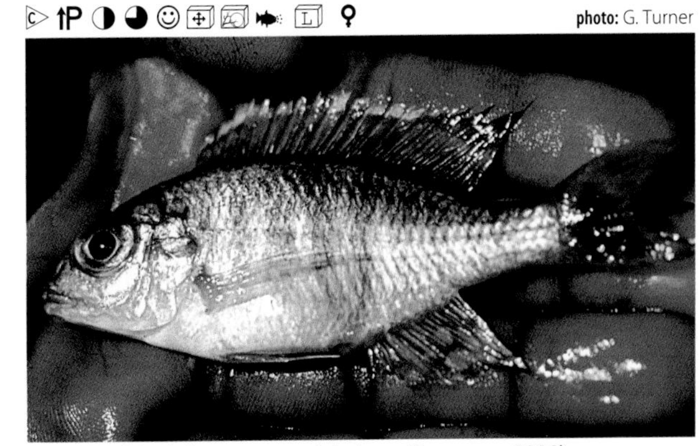

A41747-3 *Lethrinops macrophthalmus* (Boulenger, 1908)

Lake Malawi: Jalo Reef; W, 14 cm

♂ **photo:** Ad Konings

A41748-4 *Lethrinops stridei* Eccles & Lewis, 1977

Lake Malawi: SE-Arm; W, 13 cm

♂ photo: G. Turner

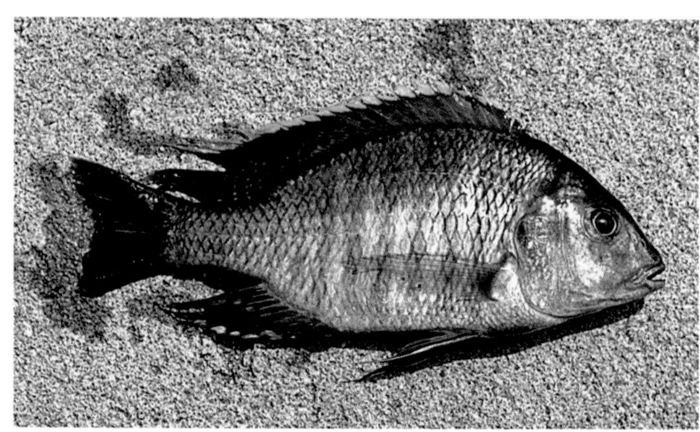

A41749-4 *Lethrinops macrochir* (Regan, 1922)

Lake Malawi, Lake Malombe; W, 16 cm

♂ photo: G. Turner

A41749-4 *Lethrinops macrochir* (Regan, 1922)

Lake Malawi, Lake Malombe; W, 16 cm

♀ photo: G. Turner

A41750-3 *Lethrinops* sp. "Blue Orange"

Lake Malawi: SE Arm; W, 8 cm

♂ photo: G. Turner

A41751-4 *Lethrinops* sp. "Yellow Tail"

Lake Malawi: SE-Arm; W, 8 cm

♂ photo: G. Turner

A41752-4 *Lethrinops* sp. "Domira Blue"

Lake Malawi: Domira Bay; W, 10.5 cm

♂ ♀ photo: G. Turner

A41753-3 *Lethrinops* sp. "Undu Point"

Lake Malawi: Undu Point; W, 10 cm

♂ photo: A. Spreinat

A41754-4 *Lethrinops* sp. "Bighead"

Lake Malawi: Ulande; W, 10 cm

♂ photo: G. Turner

A41755-4 *Lethrinops* sp. "Yellow"

Lake Malawi: SE-Arm; W, 7 cm

photo: G. Turner

A41756-4 *Lethrinops* sp. "Black Chin"

Lake Malawi: S-E-Arm; W, 9.5 cm

photo: G. Turner

A41757-5 *Lethrinops* sp. "Grey"

Lake Malawi: Mazinzi, Chiponda, SE-Arm; W, 11 cm

photo: G. Turner

A41758-4 *Placidochromis polli* (Burgess & Axelrod, 1973)*

Lake Malawi: Domira Bay; W, 19 cm

photo: G. Turner

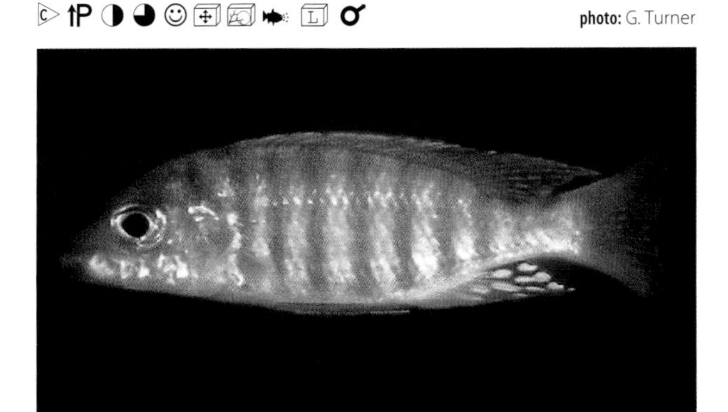

A41759-3 *Lethrinops* sp. "Maylandia Mix"

Lake Malawi: Luwala Reef; W, 10 cm

photo: Ad Konings

A41760-3 *Lethrinops* sp. "Maylandia Mix"

Lake Malawi: Kande Isl.; W, 10 cm

photo: Ad Konings

A41761-4 *Lethrinops* sp. "Matumbe"

Lake Malawi: SE-Arm; W, 11 cm

photo: G. Turner

A41761-4 *Lethrinops* sp. "Matumbe"

Lake Malawi: SE-Arm; W, 11 cm

photo: G. Turner

*This species was originally considered to be a *Lethrinops*, but was transferred to *Placidochromis* by Hanssens in Snoeks, 2004. We received that information after our layout-deadline, so the species is still illustrated here.

A41762-4 *Lethrinops altus* TREWAVAS, 1931

Lake Malawi: Thumbi East Isl.; W, 15.8 cm

photo: Ad Konings

A41763-4 *Lethrinops* sp. "Deepwater Altus"

Lake Malawi: S-E-Arm; W, 10 cm

♂

photo: G. Turner

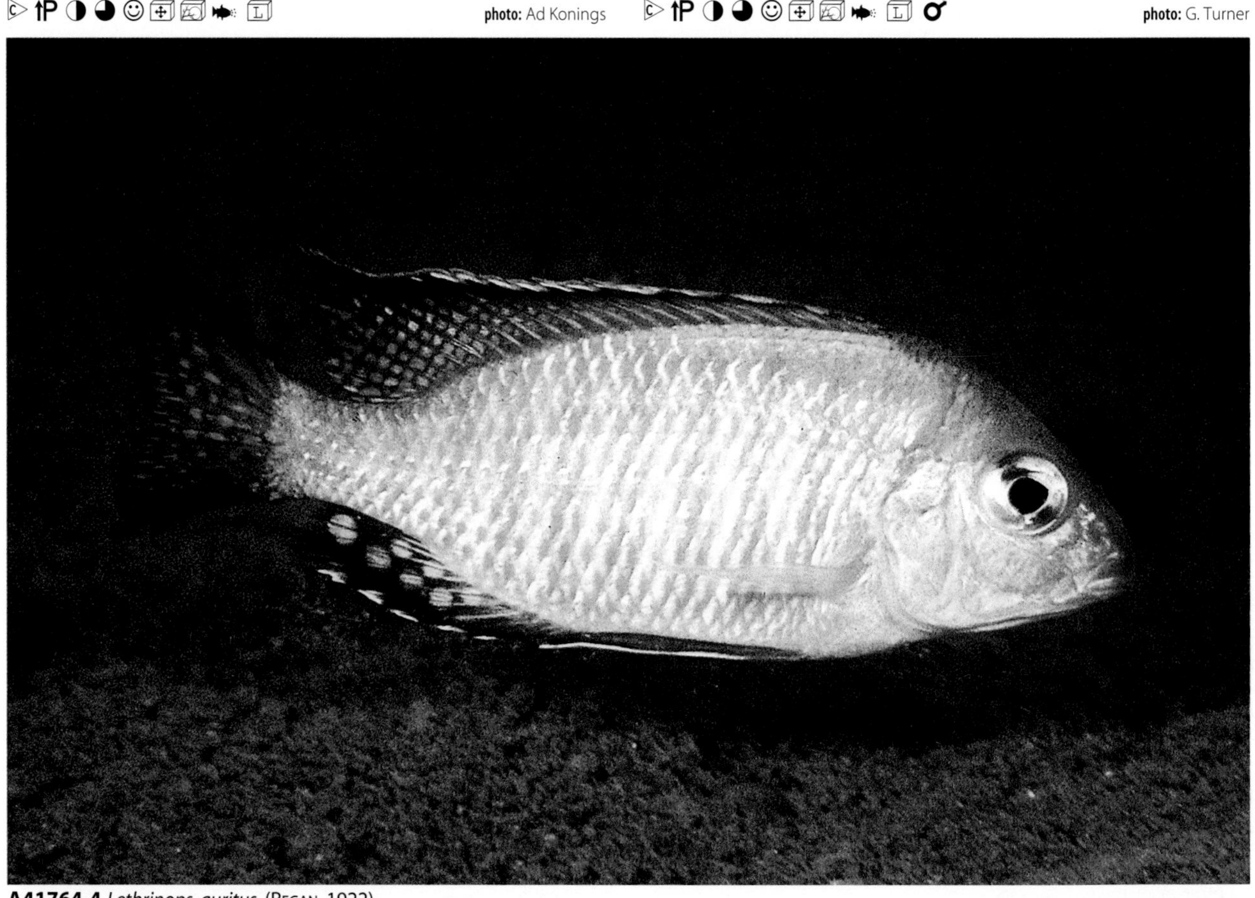

A41764-4 *Lethrinops auritus* (REGAN, 1922)

Lake Malawi: Chembwe; W, 8-14 cm

♂

photo: Ad Konings

A41765-4 *Lethrinops* sp. "Auritus Selewa"

Lake Malawi: Selewa; W, 10 cm

♂

photo: Ad Konings

A41765-3 *Lethrinops* sp. "Auritus Selewa"

Lake Malawi: Selewa; W, 10 cm

♀

photo: Ad Konings

A41766-4 *Lethrinops* sp. "Auritus Lion"

Lake Malawi: Lion's Cove; W, 8-14 cm

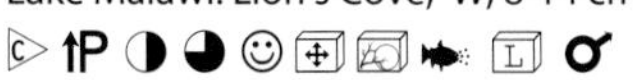

photo: Ad Konings

A41767-4 *Lethrinops microstoma* TREWAVAS, 1931

Lake Malawi; W, 15 cm

photo: E. Schraml

A41768-4 *Lethrinops microstoma* TREWAVAS, 1931

Lake Malawi: Senga Bay; W, 15 cm

photo: M. Smith

A41767-4 *Lethrinops microstoma* TREWAVAS, 1931

Lake Malawi; W, 15 cm

photo: E. Schraml

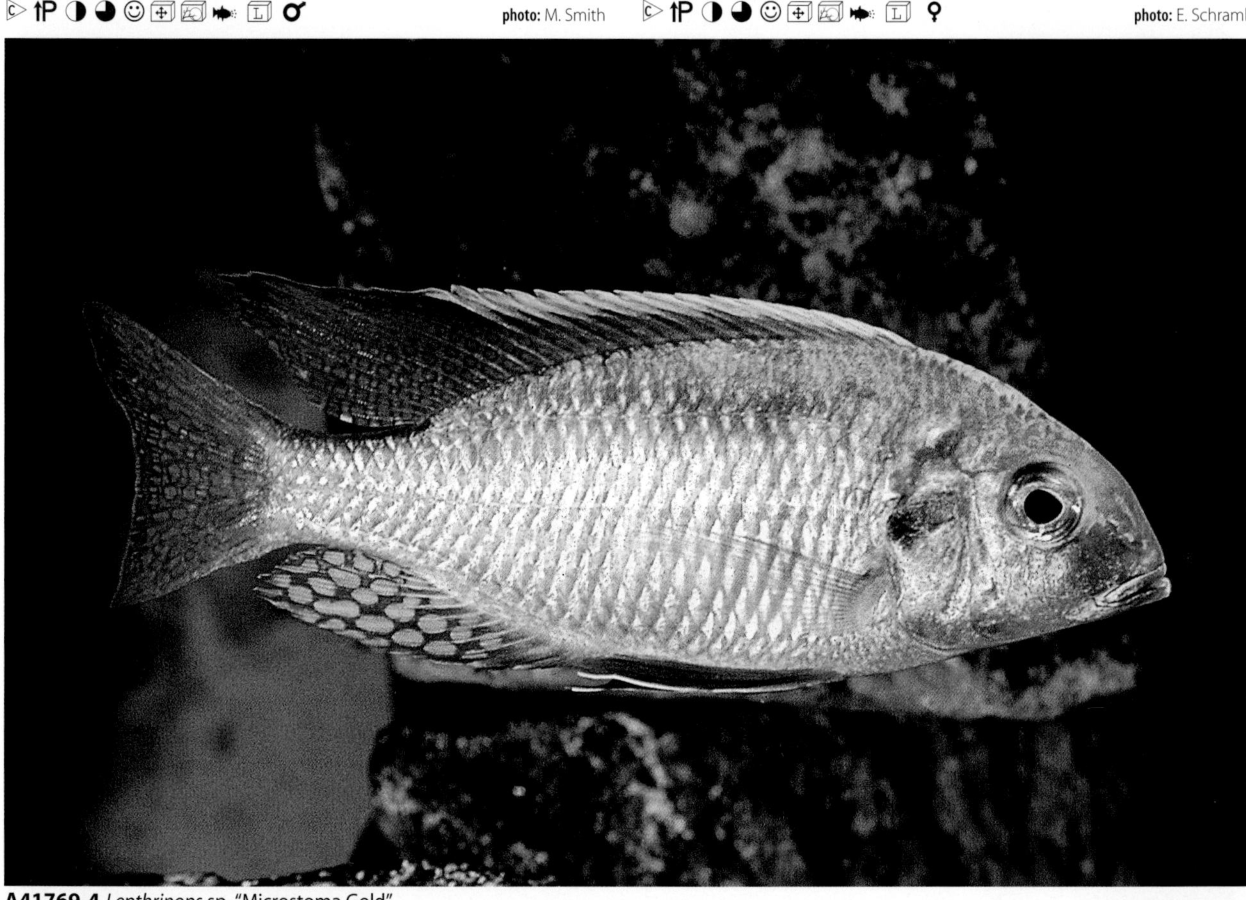

A41769-4 *Lepthrinops* sp. "Microstoma Gold"

Lake Malawi; W, 15 cm

photo: Ad Konings

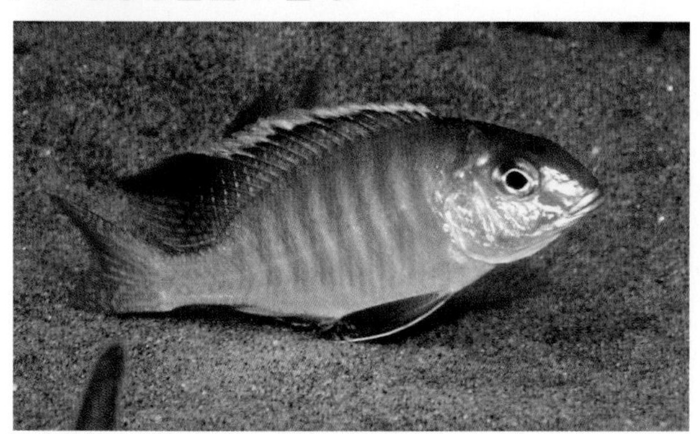

A41770-4 *Lepthrinops* sp. "Microstoma Gold"

Lake Malawi: Narungu; W, 15 cm

♂

photo: Ad Konings

A41770-4 *Lepthrinops* sp. "Microstoma Gold"

Lake Malawi: Narungu; W, 15 cm

♂

photo: Ad Konings

A41771-3 *Lethrinops* sp. "Hongi Island"

Lake Malawi: Hongi Isl./Tanzania

♂

photo: Dr. L. Seegers

A41771-3 *Lethrinops* sp."Hongi Island"

Lake Malawi: Hongi Isl./Tanzania

♀

photo: Dr. L. Seegers

A41772-5 *Lethrinops* sp. "Big Blue"

Lake Malawi: Chiuni Rock/Miluluka/Moz.; W, ? cm

photo: A. Spreinat

A41773-4 *Lethrinops* cf. *marginatus* AHL, 1926 fide KONINGS 2001
see also pp. 85 and 89
Lake Malawi: Liuli; W, 12 cm

photo: Ad Konings

A41774-4 *Lethrinops turneri* NGATUNGA & SNOEKS, 2003

Lake Malawi: S-E-Arm; W, 12 cm

photo: G. Turner

A41700-4 *Lethrinops* sp. "Yellow Collar"

Lake Malawi: Likoma Isl.; W, 10 cm ♂

photo: A. Spreinat

A41700-4 *Lethrinops* sp. "Yellow Collar"

Lake Malawi: Likoma Isl.; W, 10 cm ♀

photo: A. Spreinat

A41775-4 *Lethrinops* sp. "Yellow Collar"

Lake Malawi: Mbamba Bay/Tanzania; W, 10 cm

photo: A. Spreinat

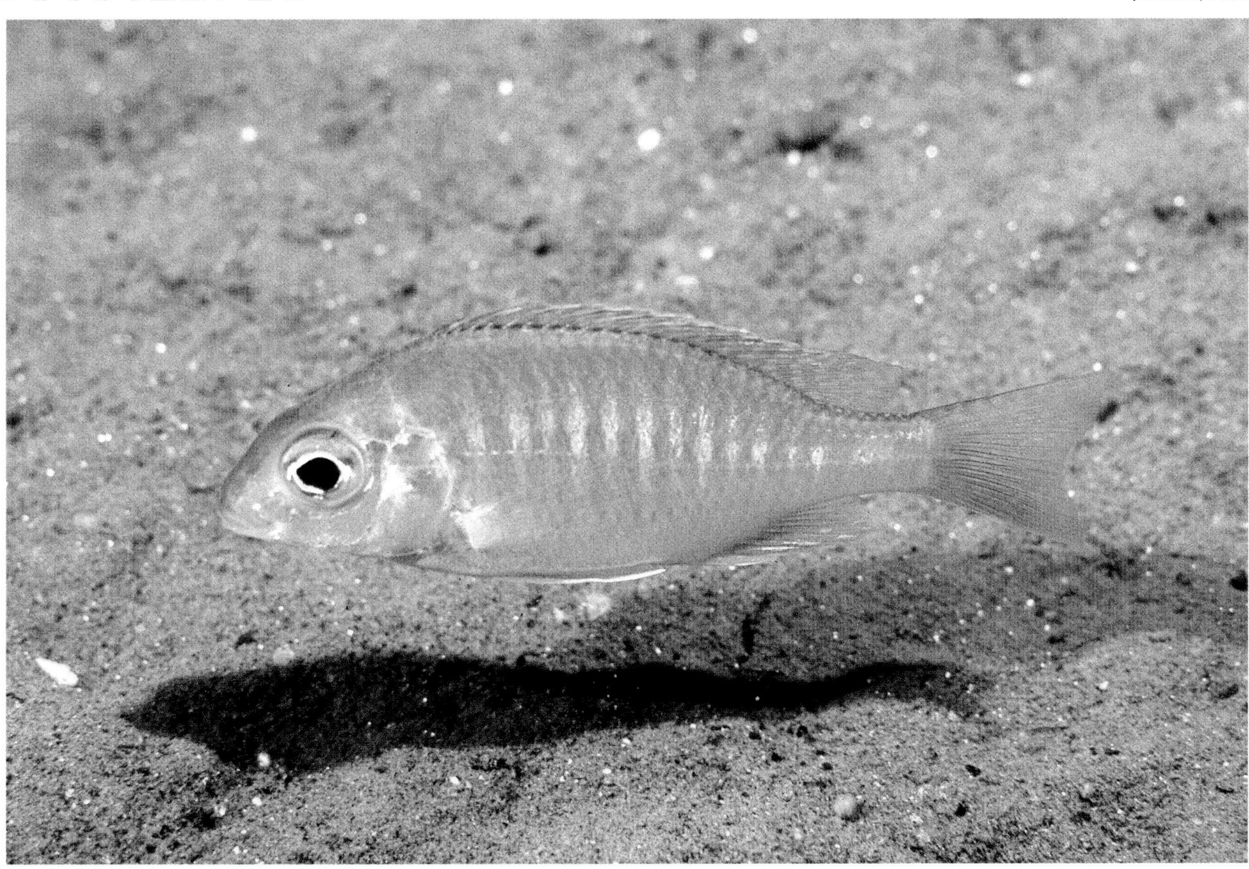

A41775-4 *Lethrinops* sp. "Yellow Collar"

Lake Malawi: Mbamba Bay/Tanzania; W, 10 cm

photo: A. Spreinat

A41776-4 *Lethrinops* sp. "Yellow Collar"

Lake Malawi: Lupingu/Tansania; W, 10 cm

photo: A. Spreinat

A41777-4 *Lethrinops* sp. "Nyassae"

Lake Malawi: Mdoka; W, 10 cm

photo: M. Smith

A41778-4 *Lethrinops leptodon* REGAN, 1922

Lake Malawi: Chiloelo; W, 20 cm

photo: Ad Konings

A41778-4 *Lethrinops leptodon* REGAN, 1922

Lake Malawi: Chiloelo; W, 20 cm

photo: Ad Konings

A41779-4 *Lethrinops leptodon* REGAN, 1922

Lake Malawi: Senga Bay; W, 20 cm

photo: Ad Konings

A41780-4 *Lethrinops christyi* TREWAVAS, 1931

Lake Malawi: S-E-Arm; W, 18.3 cm

photo: G. Turner

A89000-4 *Taeniolethrinops* sp. "Black Fin"

Lake Malawi: Mbungu/Likoma; W, 15 cm

photo: A. Spreinat

A89000-4 *Taeniolethrinops* sp. "Black Fin"

Lake Malawi: Mbungu/Likoma; W, 15 cm

photo: A. Spreinat

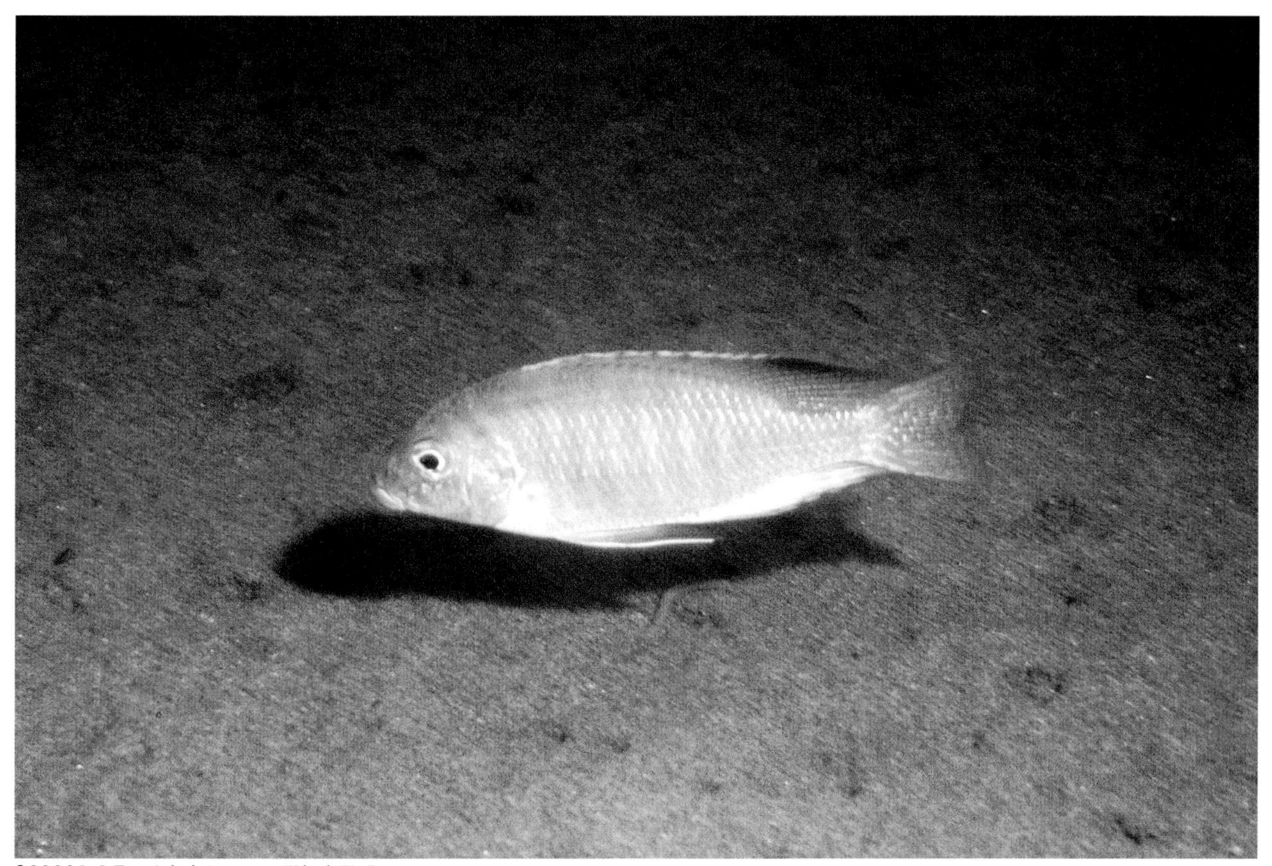

A89001-4 *Taeniolethrinops* sp. "Black Fin"

Lake Malawi: Chinyizi/Lupuchi/Moz.; W, 15 cm

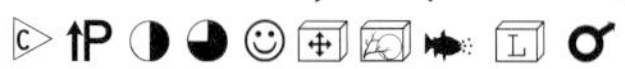

photo: A. Spreinat

A89002-4 *Taeniolethrinops* sp. "Black Fin"

Lake Malawi: Pombo Rocks/Tanzania; W, 15 cm

photo: A. Spreinat

A89000-4 *Taeniolethrinops* sp. "Black Fin"

Lake Malawi: Mbungu/Likoma; W, 15 cm

photo: A. Spreinat

A89003-4 *Taeniolethrinops* sp. "Black Fin"

Lake Malawi: Lupingu/Tanzania; W, 15 cm

photo: A. Spreinat

A89004-4 *Taeniolethrinops* sp. "Black Fin"

Lake Malawi: Mphande/Metangula/Moz.; W, 15 cm

photo: A. Spreinat

A89004-4 *Taeniolethrinops* sp. "Black Fin"

Lake Malawi: Mphande/Metangula/Moz.; W, 15 cm

photo: A. Spreinat

A89004-4 *Taeniolethrinops* sp. "Black Fin"

Lake Malawi: Mphande/Metangula/Moz.; W, 15 cm

photo: A. Spreinat

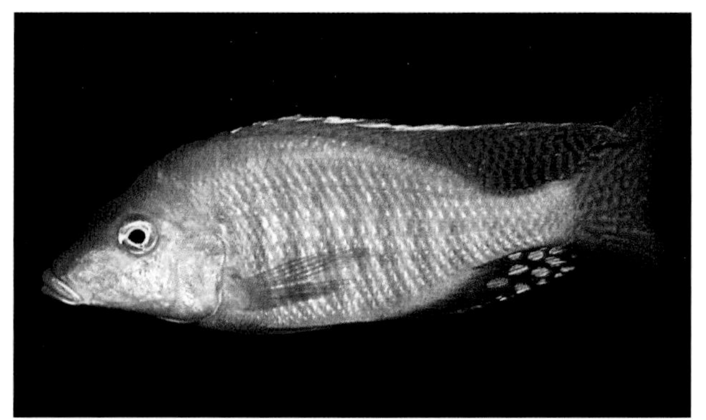

A89005-4 *Taeniolethrinops furcicauda* (TREWAVAS, 1931)

Lake Malawi: Lumessi; W, 21 cm

photo: Ad Konings

A89006-4 *Taeniolethrinops furcicauda* (TREWAVAS, 1931)

Lake Malawi: Chiofu; W, 21 cm

photo: Ad Konings

A89007-4 *Taeniolethrinops* sp. "Furcicauda Liuli"

Lake Malawi: Liuli; W, 21 cm

photo: Ad Konings

A89007-4 *Taeniolethrinops* sp. "Furcicauda Liuli"

Lake Malawi: Liuli; W, 21 cm

photo: Ad Konings

A89008-4 *Taeniolethrinops* sp. "Furcicauda Ntekete"

Lake Malawi: Ntekete; W, 21 cm

photo: Ad Konings

A89008-4 *Taeniolethrinops* sp. "Furcicauda Ntekete"

Lake Malawi: Ntekete; W, 21 cm

 ♀ **photo:** A. Spreinat

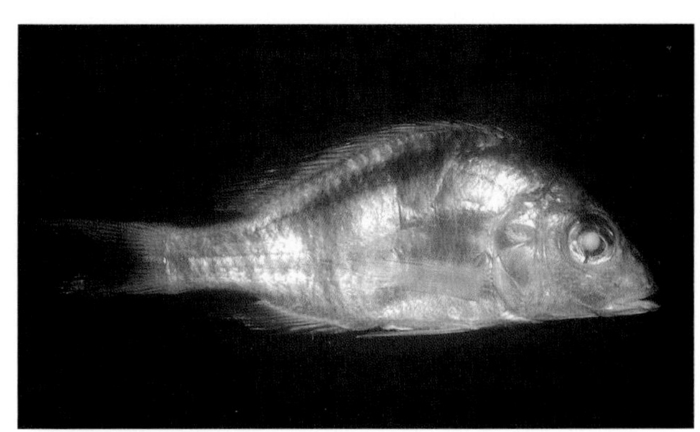

A89009-4 *Taeniolethrinops cyrtonotus* (TREWAVAS, 1931)
preserved specimen: holotype: BMNH 1930.1.31.100

Lake Malawi: W, 11.2 cm

   ♂ **photo:** E. Schraml

A89010-4 *Taeniolethrinops* sp.

Lake Malawi: Senga Bay; W, 20 cm

 ♂ **photo:** M. Smith

A89011-4 *Taeniolethrinops laticeps* (TREWAVAS, 1931)
preserved specimen: syntype: BMNH 1930.1.31.221

Lake Malawi; W, 30 cm

 ♂ **photo:** E. Schraml

A89012-4 *Taeniolethrinops* cf. *laticeps* (TREWAVAS, 1931)

Lake Malawi; W, 30 cm

♂ **photo:** A. Spreinat

A89012-3 *Taeniolethrinops* cf. *laticeps* (TREWAVAS, 1931)

Lake Malawi; W, 30 cm

photo: A. Spreinat

A89013-4 *Taeniolethrinops* sp. "Laticeps Itungi"

Lake Malawi: Liuli; W, 30 cm

photo: L. DeMason

A89014-4 *Taeniolethrinops* sp.

Lake Malawi: Ngulu/Chiloelo/Moz., W, 30 cm

photo: A. Spreinat

A89015-4 *Taeniolethrinops praeorbitalis* (REGAN, 1922)

Lake Malawi: Senga Bay; W, 30 cm

photo: M. Smith

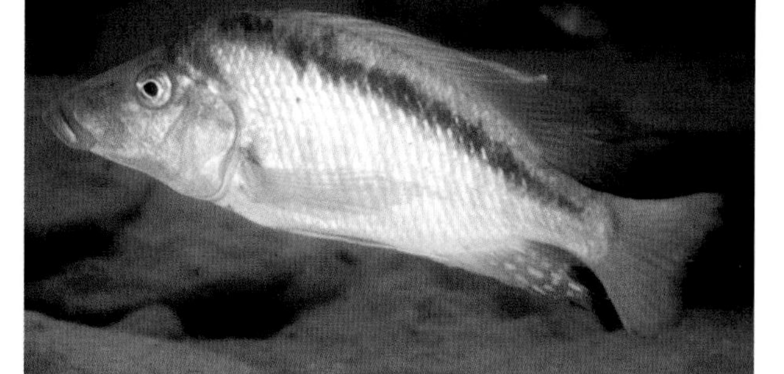

A89016-4 *Taeniolethrinops praeorbitalis* (REGAN, 1922)

Lake Malawi: Nangunji/Moz.; W, 30 cm

photo: A. Spreinat

A89017-4 *Taeniolethrinops praeorbitalis* (REGAN, 1922)

Lake Malawi; W, 30 cm

photo: E. Schraml

A89017-4 *Taeniolethrinops praeorbitalis* (REGAN, 1922)

Lake Malawi; W, 30 cm

photo: A. Spreinat

A89018-4 *Taeniolethrinops* sp.

Lake Malawi: Mbenji Isl.; W, 30 cm

photo: A. Spreinat

Malawicichliden bei Otter Point.
Malawi cichlids near Otter Point.

photo: E. Klaban

Mit jeder

Aqualog - *news*

internationale Zeitschrift für Aquarianer

erscheinen als **stickups** Ergänzungen
mit neuen Fischbildern, die Sie

hier

einkleben sollten, damit Sie immer "up-to-date" sind.

With every

Aqualog - *news*

international journal for aquarists

you will find **stickups** as supplements
which should be sticked in

here

to make sure that you are always up-to-date

Aqualog
im Internet
http:// www. aqualog. de

mit Informationen zu den Ergänzungen und Neuerscheinungen

Aqualog
in the Internet
http:// www. aqualog. de

with informations about the supplements and new publications

Mit jeder
Aqualog - *news*
internationale Zeitschrift für Aquarianer
erscheinen als **stickups** Ergänzungen
mit neuen Fischbildern, die Sie

hier

einkleben sollten, damit Sie immer "up-to-date" sind.

With every
Aqualog - *news*
international journal for aquarists
you will find **stickups** as supplements
which should be sticked in

here

to make sure that you are always up-to-date

Aqualog
im Internet
http:// www. aqualog. de

mit Informationen zu den Ergänzungen und
Neuerscheinungen

Aqualog
in the Internet
http:// www. aqualog. de

with informations about the supplements and
new publications

Mit jeder

Aqualog - *news*

internationale Zeitschrift für Aquarianer

erscheinen als **stickups** Ergänzungen
mit neuen Fischbildern, die Sie

hier

einkleben sollten, damit Sie immer "up-to-date" sind.

With every

Aqualog - *news*

international journal for aquarists

you will find **stickups** as supplements
which should be sticked in

here

to make sure that you are always up-to-date

Aqualog
im Internet
http:// www. aqualog. de

mit Informationen zu den Ergänzungen und
Neuerscheinungen

Aqualog
in the Internet
http:// www. aqualog. de

with informations about the supplements and
new publications

Literatur
Literature

Baasch, P. (1992): Lethrinops micrentodon (Regan, 1922), p. 50 in: Konings A. (ed.): Cichlidenjahrbuch Bd. 2, Cichlid Press, St. Leon-Rot, Deutschland.

Baensch, H. A. & Riehl, R. (1985): Aquarien Atlas. Aquarien-Atlas Bd. 2, Melle, Germany, 1216 pp.

Eccles, D.H. & Lewis, D.S.C. (1977): A taxonomic study of the genus Lethrinops Regan (Pisces: Cichlidae) from Lake Malawi, Part 1. Ichthyol. Bull. JLB Smith Inst. Ichthyol., No 36: 1-12.

Eccles, D.H. & Lewis, D.S.C. (1978): A taxonomic study of the genus Lethrinops Regan (Pisces: Cichlidae) from Lake Malawi, Part 2. Ichthyol. Bull. JLB Smith Inst. Ichthyol., No 37: 1-11.

Eccles, D.H. & Lewis, D.S.C. (1979): A taxonomic study of the genus Lethrinops Regan (Pisces: Cichlidae) from Lake Malawi, Part 3. Ichthyol. Bull. JLB Smith Inst. Ichthyol., No 38: 1-25.

Eccles, D.H. & Trewavas, E. (1989): Malawian Cichlid Fishes: A Classification of Some Haplochromine Genera. Lake Fish Movies: Herten, Germany, 335 pp.

Günther, A. (1894): Second report on the reptiles, batrachians, and fishes transmitted by Mr. H. H. Johnston, C. B., from British Central Africa. Proc. Zool. Soc. Lond. 1893 (pt 4): 616-628, Pls. 53-57.

Hanssens, M. (2004): The deep-water Placidochromis species. pp. 104-197 in: Snoeks, J. (ed.): The cichlid diversity of Lake Malawi/Nyasa/Niassa: identification, distribution and taxonomy. Cichlid Press, El Paso, 360 pp.

Hauser, L., Idid, M.R., Harley, M., Shaw, P.W., and Carvalho, G.R. (1999): Molecular genetics of Lake Malawi/Nyasa cichlids. p. 164-179 in A.J. Ribbink and A.C. Ribbink, eds. SADC/GEF Lake Malawi/Nyasa/Niassa Biodiversity Conservation Project. Extended Abstracts. SADC/GEF Project, Senga Bay.

Hermann, W. (1997): Ein Sandflächenbewohner aus dem Malawisee. Aquaristik aktuell, 2: 54-55

Höltje, A. (1988): Lethrinops auritus REGAN, 1921. DCG-Info 19(4): 72-75

Konings, A. (1990): Cichlids and all the other fishes of Lake Malawi. TFH Publications, Neptune City, New Jersey, 495 pp.

Konings, A. (1994): Die vielen Gesichter des Aulonocara stuartgranti, pp. 38-41 in: Konings, A. (ed.): Cichlidenjahrbuch Bd. 4, Cichlid Press, St. Leon-Rot, Germany.

Konings, A. (1995): A review of the sand-dwelling species of the genus Aulonocara, with a description of three new species. pp. 26-36 in Konings, A. (ed.) The Cichlids Yearbook, Vol.5, Cichlid Press, St. Leon-Rot, Germany.

Lewis, D.; Reinthal, P. & Trendall, J. (1986): A Guide to the Fishes of Lake Malawl National Park. WWF, Gland, Switzerland, 71 pp.

Lippitsch, E. (1993): A phyletic study on lacustrine haplochromine fishes (Perciformes, Cichlidae) of East Africa, based on scale and squamation characters. Journal of Fish Biology 42: 903-946.

Meyer, M.K. , Riehl, R. & Zetzsche, H. (1987): A revision of the cichlid fishes of the genus Aulonocara Regan, 1921 from Lake Malawi, with descriptions of six new species. (Cour. Forsch-Inst. Senckenberg, 94, 7-54)

Ngatunga, B.P. (2000): A taxonomic revision of the shallow-water species of the genera Lethrinops, Tramitichromis and Taeniolethrinops (Teleostei, Cichlidae) from Lake Malawi/Nyasa/Niassa (East Africa). Unpublished Ph.D. thesis, Rhodes University, South Africa, 293 pp.

Reitz, E. (1992): Aulonocara rostratum Trewavas, 1935, p. 46 in: Konings, A. (ed.): Cichlidenjahrbuch Bd. 2, Cichlid Press, St. Leon-Rot, Germany.

Ribbink, A.J.; Marsh, A.C.; Marsh, B.A.; Ribbink, A.C. & Sharp, B.J. (1983): A preliminary survey of the cichlid fishes of rocky habitats in Lake Malawi. (S. Afr. J. Zool., 18: 149-309)

Schoop, E. (1977): Beobachtungen an Aulonocara nyassae (REGAN, 1921), dem Kaiserbuntbarsch. DCG-Info (12): 231-232.

Snoeks, J. (2000): How well known is the Ichthyodiversity of the Large East African Lakes? (Advances in Ecological Research, Vol.31, 17-38)

Snoeks, J. (2001): Cichlid diversity, speciation and systematics: examples from the Great African Lakes. (Journal of Aquariculture and Aquatic Sciences, Cichlid Research: State of the Art, Vol. IX: 150-166)

Snoeks, J. (ed.) (2004): The cichlid diversity of Lake Malawi/Nyasa/Niassa: identification, distribution and taxonomy. Cichlid Press, El Paso, 360 pp.

Snoeks, J., and Walapa, R. (1999): Chapter 8. The genus Alticorpus Stauffer & McKaye, 1988. 27 pp in J. Snoeks (ed.): Report on Systematics and Taxonomy. SADC/GEF Project, Senga Bay.

Snoeks, J. and Walapa, R. (2004): The genus Alticorpus Stauffer & McKaye, 1988. pp. 27-56 in: Snoeks, J. (ed.): The cichlid diversity of Lake Malawi/Nyasa/Niassa: identification, distribution and taxonomy. Cichlid Press, El Paso, 360 pp.

Spreinat, A. (1989): Kaiserbuntbarsche des Malawisees. Ulmer Verlag, Stuttgart, 106 pp.

Spreinat, A.(2002): Aulonocara baenschi. DATZ/Aq.-Praxis, 55 (4): 2-4

Spreinat, A. (2004): Zur Taxonomie der Aulonocara-baenschi-Gruppe. Teil 1. DCG-Info 35 (4): 73-81.

Spreinat, A. (2004): Zur Taxonomie der Aulonocara-baenschi-Gruppe. Teil 2. DCG-Info 35 (6): 130-139.

Staeck, W. (1974): Der Kaiserbuntbarsch - ein Neuer aus dem Malawisee. Aquar. Mag. 8(9): 368-370

Staeck, W. (1988) : Kaiserbuntbarsche. Die Gattung Aulonocara Regan, 1922. 2. Stammbaum und Ökologie. (DATZ 41 (8): 296-299)

Staeck, W. (2000): Gescheckte Kaiserbuntbarsche? DATZ 53(2): 18-21

Stauffer, J.R. & Kellogg, K.A. (1996): Partnerwahl bei Malawicichliden. pp 23-28 in: Das Cichlidenjahrbuch, Bd.6, Lauenau, Germany.

Tawil, P. (2003): Aulonocara koningsi n. sp., un cichlidé nouveau du lac Malawi apparanté à Aulonocara stuartgranti (Pisces, Teleostei, Cichlidae). L' an Cichlidé 3: 89-98.

Tawil, P. & Allgayer, R. (1987): Description de *Aulonocara maylandi kandeensis* subsp. n. (Pisces, Cichlidae) du lac Malawi. Cybium v. 11 (no. 2): 159-166, 1 col. pl.

Trewavas, E. (1984): Un nom et une description pour l'Aulonocara „sulphur-head", poisson cichlid, du Lac Malawi (Rev.fr. Aquariol.,11(1):7-10)

Turner, G. (1996): Offshore Cichlids of Lake Malawi. Cichlid Press, Lauenau, Germany, 240 pp.

Ulrich, M. (1998): Ein kleiner Sandburgenbauer aus dem Malawisee: Lethrinops „Micrentodon Makokola". DCG-Info 29(12): 221-224

Wessels, M. (2003): Playing the flute. Today's Fishkeeper, 2: 56-58

Winkelmann, H. (2000): Gescheckte Kaiserbuntbarsche: Problemfische für die DCG? DCG-Info 31(5): 105-110.

Checkliste der in diesem Band behandelten nominellen Arten und Gattungen.
Checklist of the nominal species and genera dealt with in this volume.

Alticorpus geoffreyi Snoeks & Walapa, 2004
type locality: North end of SW and SE Arms, Transact from Chipoka to Makanjila, Lake Malawi.

Alticorpus macrocleithrum (Stauffer & McKaye, 1985).
original name: *Cyrtocara macrocleithrum*
type locality: Cape Maclear, Lake Malawi, Malawi, Africa, 14°04'S, 34°45'E, 75 m.

Alticorpus mentale Stauffer & McKaye, 1988.
type locality: Off Monkey Bay, Lake Malawi, 13°56'S, 34°52'E, 75 m.

Alticorpus pectinatum Stauffer & McKaye, 1988.
type locality: Off Monkey Bay, Lake Malawi [Lake Nyasa], Africa, 13°56'S, 34°52'E, 75 m.
Synonym of *Alticorpus peterdaviesi*

Alticorpus peterdaviesi (Burgess & Axelrod, 1973).
original name: *Trematocranus peterdaviesi*
type locality: Off Monkey Bay, Lake Malawi [Lake Nyasa], se. Africa, 43 fm.

Alticorpus profundicola Stauffer & McKaye, 1988.
type locality: Off Nkota Kota, Lake Malawi, 159 m.

Astatotilapia calliptera (Günther, 1894).
original name: *Chromis callipterus*
type locality: Lake Malawi [Lake Nyasa].

Astatotilapia tweddlei Jackson, 1985.
type locality: Near Kachulu, Lake Chilwa, Malawi.

Aulonocara aquilonium Konings, 1995.
type locality: Mdoka, Malawi

Aulonocara auditor (Trewavas, 1935).
original name: *Trematocranus auditor*
type locality:Vua, Lake Malawi [Lake Nyasa]

Aulonocara baenschi Meyer & Riehl, 1985.
type locality: Nkhomo, 8 km west of Benga, Lake Malawi

Aulonocara brevinidus Konings, 1995.
type locality:South of Nsinje R., Msinje, Malawi.

Aulonocara brevirostris (Trewavas, 1935).
original name: *Trematocranus brevirostris*
type locality: Bar House, Lake Malawi [Lake Nyasa]

Aulonocara ethelwynnae Meyer, Riehl & Zetzsche, 1987.
type locality: Chitande [Chitendi] I., Lake Malawi

Aulonocara gertrudae Konings, 1995.
type locality: South of Nsinje R., Masinje, Malawi.

Aulonocara guentheri Eccles,1989.
type locality: Lake Malawi [Lake Nyasa]

Aulonocara hansbaenschi Meyer, Riehl & Zetzsche ,1987.
type locality: 8 km south of Masinje, e. Lake Malawi , Malawi.

Aulonocara hueseri Meyer, Riehl & Zetzsche, 1987.
type locality: East coast of Likoma I., Lake Malawi , Malawi.

Aulonocara jacobfreibergi (Johnson 1974).
original name: *Trematocranus jacobfreibergi*
type locality: Off Makanjila, Lake Malawi.

Aulonocara kandeensis Tawil & Allgayer, 1987.
original name: *Aulonocara maylandi kandeensis*
type locality: Kande I., Lake Malawi.

Aulonocara koningsi Tawil, 2003.
type locality: Mbenji Isl., Lake Malawi.

Aulonocara korneliae Meyer, Riehl & Zetzsche, 1987.
type locality: East coast of Chisumulu I., Lake Malawi, Malawi.

Aulonocara macrochir Trewavas 1935
type locality: Monkey Bay, Lake Malawi

Aulonocara maylandi Trewavas, 1984.
type locality: Eccles Reef, near Makanjila Point, e. shore of Lake Malawi.

Aulonocara nyassae Regan, 1922.
Lake Malawi [Lake Nyasa].

Aulonocara rostratum Trewavas, 1935
type locality: Vua, Lake Malawi [Lake Nyasa].

Aulonocara saulosi Meyer, Riehl & Zetzsche, 1987.
type locality: 8 km south of Masinje, east coast of Lake Malawi.

Aulonocara steveni Meyer, Riehl & Zetzsche, 1987
type locality: Kande I., Lake Malawi, Malawi.

Aulonocara stonemani (Burgess & Axelrod, 1973).
original name: *Placidochromis stonemani*
type locality: off Monkey Bay, Lake Malawi.

Aulonocara stuartgranti Meyer & Riehl, 1985.
type locality: Mpanga Rocks, Chilumba, Lake Malawi, Malawi.

Aulonocara trematocephala (Boulenger, 1901).
original name: *Tilapia trematocephala*
Lake Malawi [Lake Nyasa], [not north end of Lake Tanganyika].

Cleithrochromis bowleyi Eccles in Axelrod, 1974
Not available, no distinguishing features.
The picture shows *Alticorpus macrocleithrum*.

Haplochromis centropristoides Nichols & La Monte, 1931.
type locality: Karonga, Lake Malawi [Lake Nyasa], Malawi.
Synonym of *Astatotilapia calliptera*.

Lethrinops albus Regan, 1922
type locality: Lake Malawi [Lake Nyasa].

Lethrinops altus Trewavas, 1931.
type locality: Lake Malawi [Lake Nyasa].

Lethrinops argenteus Ahl, 1926.
type locality: Near Langenburg, Lake Malawi [Lake Nyasa].

Lethrinops auritus (Regan, 1922).
original name: *Haplochromis auritus*
type locality: Lake Malawi [Lake Nyasa].

Lethrinops borealis Eccles & Lewis, 1979
original name: *Lethrinops mylodon borealis*
type locality: Nkhata Bay, Lake Malawi , 11°36'S, 34°18'E, ca. 50 fm.

Lethrinops christyi Trewavas, 1931.
type locality: Monkey Bay, Lake Malawi [Lake Nyasa].

Lethrinops fasciatus AHL, 1926.
type locality: Near Langenburg, Lake Malawi [Lake Nyasa].
Synonym of *Taeniolethrinops praeorbitalis*

Lethrinops furcifer TREWAVAS, 1931.
type locality: Lake Malawi [Lake Nyasa].

Lethrinops gossei BURGESS & AXELROD ,1973.
type locality: Off Monkey Bay, Lake Malawi, 43 fm.

Lethrinops leptodon REGAN, 1922
type locality: Lake Malawi [Lake Nyasa].

Lethrinops lethrinus (GÜNTHER 1894).
original name: *Chromis lethrinus*
type locality: Lake Malawi [Lake Nyasa].

Lethrinops longimanus TREWAVAS, 1931.
type locality: Between Malembo (14°13'S, 34°48'E) and Bar House (14°23'S, 35°12'E), s. Lake Malawi [Lake Nyasa].

Lethrinops longipinnis ECCLES & LEWIS, 1978.
type locality: Lake Malawi, 14°02'S, 34°58'E, 40 fm.

Lethrinops lunaris TREWAVAS, 1931.
type locality: Lake Malawi [Lake Nyasa].

Lethrinops macracanthus TREWAVAS, 1931.
type locality: Lake Malawi [Lake Nyasa].

Lethrinops macrochir (REGAN, 1922).
original name: *Haplochromis macrochir*
type locality: Lake Malawi [Lake Nyasa].

Lethrinops macrophthalmus (BOULENGER, 1908).
original name: *Tilapia macrophthalma*
type locality: Lake Malawi [Lake Nyasa].

Lethrinops macrorhynchus REGAN, 1922
type locality: Lake Malawi [Lake Nyasa].
Synonym of *Taeniolethrinops praeorbitalis*

Lethrinops marginatus AHL, 1926.
type locality: Near Langenburg, Lake Malawi [Lake Nyasa].

Lethrinops micrentodon (REGAN, 1922).
original name: *Haplochromis micrentodon*
type locality: Lake Malawi [Lake Nyasa].

Lethrinops microdon ECCLES & LEWIS, 1977.
type locality: Off Monkey Bay, Lake Malawi, 14°03'S, 34°56'E, 30 fm.

Lethrinops microstoma TREWAVAS, 1931.
type locality: Lake Malawi [Lake Nyasa].

Lethrinops mylodon ECCLES & LEWIS, 1979.
type locality: East of Monkey Bay, 14°04'S, 34°58'E, Lake Malawi, 30-40 fm.

Lethrinops oculatus TREWAVAS, 1931.
type locality: Lake Malawi [Lake Nyasa].
Synonym of *Lethrinops marginatus*

Lethrinops parvidens TREWAVAS, 1931.
type locality: Lake Malawi [Lake Nyasa].
Eastern Africa: Lake Malawi. Habitat: freshwater.

Lethrinops stridei ECCLES & LEWIS, 1977.
type locality: Lake Malawi , 14°19'S, 35°11'E, 12 fm.

Lethrinops turneri NGATUNGA & SNOEKS, 2003.
type locality: Mvera beach, Lake Malombe, Malawi.

Neochromis simotes nyassae BORODIN, 1936
type locality: Mwaya, Lake Malawi [Lake Nyasa], Tanzania.
Synonym of *Astatotilapia calliptera*.

Otopharynx brevirostris (TREWAVAS, 1935).
original name: *Trematocranus brevirostris*
type locality: Bar House, Lake Malawi [Lake Nyasa]

Placidochromis polli (BURGESS & AXELROD, 1973)
original name: *Lethrinops polli*
type locality: Off Monkey Bay, Lake Malawi, se. Africa, 43 fm.

Taeniolethrinops cyrtonotus (TREWAVAS, 1931).
original name: *Lethrinops cyrtonotus*
type locality: Lake Malawi [Lake Nyasa].

Taeniolethrinops furcicauda (TREWAVAS, 1931)
original name: *Lethrinops furcicauda.*
type locality: Lake Malawi [Lake Nyasa].

Taeniolethrinops laticeps (TREWAVAS, 1931).
original name: *Lethrinops laticeps.*
type locality: Lake Malawi [Lake Nyasa].

Taeniolethrinops praeorbitalis (REGAN, 1922).
original name: Haplochromis praeorbitalis.
type locality: Lake Malawi [Lake Nyasa].

Tramitichromis brevis (BOULENGER, 1908).
original name: *Tilapia brevis.*
type locality: Lake Malawi [Lake Nyasa].

Tramitichromis intermedius (TREWAVAS, 1935).
original name: *Lethrinops intermedia.*
type locality: South West Arm or Fort Johnson, Monkey Bay, Lake Malawi [Lake Nyasa], se. Africa.

Tramitichromis lituris (TREWAVAS, 1931).
original name: *Lethrinops lituris.*
type locality: Lake Malawi [Lake Nyasa].

Tramitichromis trilineata (TREWAVAS, 1931).
original name: *Lethrinops trilineata.*
type locality: Lake Malawi [Lake Nyasa].

Tramitichromis variabilis (TREWAVAS, 1931).
original name: *Lethrinops variabilis.*
type locality: Vua and Mwaya, Lake Malawi [Lake Nyasa].

Index Codenummern

Index code numbers

Index alphabetisch

Index alphabetical

Symbole

Um der weltweiten Sprachenvielfalt gerecht zu werden, haben wir bewußt auf ausführlichere Texte verzichtet und ersetzen diese durch leicht einprägsame internationale Symbole, mit deren Hilfe jeder die Eigenschaften und Pflegebedingungen der Fische erkennen kann.
Die angegebenen Pflegesymbole beziehen sich auf die Haltungsbedingungen im Aquarium, nicht auf die Werte im Herkunftsland oder Biotop.

Jrsprung

sehen Sie ganz leicht an dem Buchstaben vor der
de-Nummer
= Afrika **E** = Europa N = Nordamerika
= Lateinamerika **X** = Asien + Australien

Alter

e letzte Zahl der Code-Nummer steht immer für
s Alter des fotografierten Fisches:
= small (Baby / Jugendfärbung)
= medium (Jungfisch/juvenil/Verkaufsgröße)
= large (halbwüchsig/gute Verkaufsgröße)
= XL (ausgewachsen/adult)
= XXL (Zucht-Tier/breeder)
= show (Schau-Tier/show-fish)

Herkunft

= Wild-Form **B** = Nachzucht/bred
= Zucht-Form/breeding-form
= Kreuzungs-Form/cross-bred

Größe

cm = ungefähre Größe, die dieser Fisch
sgewachsen (adult) erreichen kann.

Geschlecht

männlich ♀ weiblich ♂♀ Paar

emperatur

18–22°C (64–72°F) (Zimmertemperatur)
22–25°C (72–77°F) (tropische Fische)
24–29°C (75–85°F) (Discus etc.)
10–22°C (50–72°F) kalt (Nordamerika/Europa)

H-Wert

pH 6,5–7,2 keine besonderen Ansprüche (neutral)
pH 5,8–6,5 liebt weiches und leicht saures Wasser
pH 7,5–8,5 liebt hartes und alkalisches Wasser

eleuchtung

hell, viel Licht / Sonne
nicht zu hell
fast dunkel

utter:

Allesfresser, Trockenfutter, keine besonderen Ansprüche
Futter-Spezialist, Lebendfutter, Gefrierfutter
Fisch-Räuber, Futterfische füttern
Pflanzenfresser, Pflanzenkost zufüttern

Schwimmverhalten

keine besonderen Eigenschaften
im oberen Bereich/Oberflächen-Fisch
im unteren Bereich/Boden-Fisch

Aquarium-Einrichtung

nur Bodengrund und Steine etc.
Steine/Wurzeln/Höhlen
Pflanzen-Aquarium + Steine/Wurzeln

Verhalten/Vermehrung

Paarweise oder im Trio halten
Schwarmfisch, nicht unter 10 Exemplaren halten
Eierleger
Lebendgebärer
Maulbrüter
Höhlenbrüter
Schaumnestbauer
Algenvertilger/Scheibenputzer (Wurzeln+Spinat)
leichte Pflege (für entsprechende Gesellschaftsbecken)
schwierig zu halten, vorher Fachliteratur beachten
Vorsicht, extrem schwierig,
nur für erfahrene Spezialisten
die Eier benötigen eine spezielle Behandlung
§ geschützte Art, (WA),
„CITES" Sondergenehmigung nötig
~L~ amphibisch (benötigt Landteil)
<Bw> Brackwasser (Wasser + Salzzusatz)
~Sw~ Meerwasser (ständig im Meer lebend)
<~Sw~ juvenil im Meer (später auch im Brack- oder Süßwasser)
~Sw~> juvenil im Süßwasser (später auch im Meer)
<~Sw~> sowohl im Meer als auch im Süßwasser (wechselt!)

Mindest-Becken		Länge	Inhalt
SS	sehr klein / super small	20–40 cm	5–20 l
S	klein / small	40–80 cm	40–80 l
m	mittel / medium	60–100 cm	80–200 l
L	groß / large	100–200 cm	200–400 l
XL	sehr groß / XL	200–400 cm	400–3 000 l
XXL	extrem groß / XXL	über 400 cm	über 3 000 l (Schauaquarien)

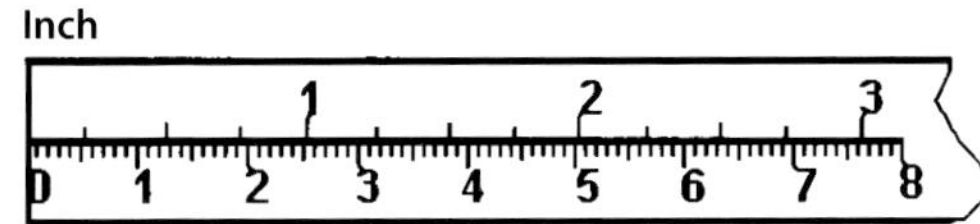

Símbolos

Teniendo en cuenta la enorme variedad de lenguas a nivel mundial, hemos decidido, intencionadamente, sustituir cualquier descripción textual detallada por símbolos internacionales. De esta forma se pueden obtener los datos más importantes, sobre las especies y su cuidado. Los símbolos sobre el cuidado siempre hacen referencia a las condiciones en acuario y no a las del pais de origen ó de los biotopos.

Continente de origen

Simplemente, fijese en la letra que va delante del código numérico

A = Africa **E** = Europa **N** = Norte America
S = Latino America **X** = Asia/Australia

Edad

El último número del código siempre significa la edad del pez

1 = muy pequeño (alevin /juvenil pequeño)
2 = pequeño (juvenil/tamaño comercial)
3 = mediano (sub-adulto/buen tamaño conercial)
4 = grande (adulto/tamaño de cria)
5 = extra grande (adulto totalmente desarrollado)
6 = excepcionalmente grande (especimen de exposición)

Procedencia

W = salvaje **B** = criado en acuario
Z = forma de cria (variedad "artificial") **X** = híbrido

Tamaño

... cm = tamaño aproximado que el pez puede alcanzar de adulto.

Sexo

♂ macho ♀ hembra  pareja

Temperatura

18–22°C(64–72°F) (temperatura ambiente)
22–25°C (72–77°F) (muchos de los peces tropicales)
24–29°C (75–85°F) (Discos etc.)
10–22°C (50–72°F) (agua fria/templada; p.e. Norte America/Europa)

Valor de pH

pH 6,5–7,2 Sin necesidades especiales (neutro)
pH 5,8–6,5 prefiere agua blanda, ligeramente ácido
pH 7,5–8,5 prefere agua dura y alcalina

Iluminación

○ brillante. Mucha luz/sol
◑ no demasiado intensa
◕ muy tenue

Alimentación

☺ omnivoros; alimento seco, sin necesidades especiales
☺ dieta especial; alimento vivo y congelado
☹ piscívoro; se alimenta de peces vivos
⊕ herbivoro; necesita alimento vegetal

Nivel de natación

aguas medias/todos los niveles
capas superficiales/nadador de superficie
capas inferiore/nadador de fondo

Decoración del acuario

Sólo rocas y el sustrato
Rocas y raices, cuevas
Acuario plantado con rocas y raices

Comportamiento/Reproducción

mantener en parejas o trios
Pez de cardumen, no mantener menos de 10 ejemplares
Ovíparo
Vivíparo
Incubador bucal
criador en cuevas
Constructor de nidos de burbujas
comedor de algas/limpiacristales (raices + alimento vegetal)
pez no agresivo, fácil de mantener (acuario comunitario)
difícil de mantener, leer previamente literatura especializada
cuidado, extremádamente dificil, solo para especialistas experimentados
los huevos necesitan cuidados específicos
§ especies protegidas (WA), se necesitan permisos especiales ("CITES")
~L~ anfibios (necesitan zona de tierra)
<Bw> agua salobre (añadir sal al agua)
~Sw~ marino (vive en el mar)
<~Sw~ juvenil en el mar (después tanto en agua salobre como en agua dulce
~Sw~> juvenil en agua dulce (después en el mar)
<~Sw~> tanto en el mar como en agua dulce (cambia!)

Tamaño mínimo de acuario

SS	super pequeño	20–40 cm	5–20 l
S	pequeño	40–80 cm	40 –80 l
m	mediano	60–100 cm	80–200 l
L	grande	100–200 cm	200–400 l
XL	XL	200–400 cm	400–3 000 l
XXL	XXL	más de 400 cm	más de 3 000 l

(Acuarios de exposición)

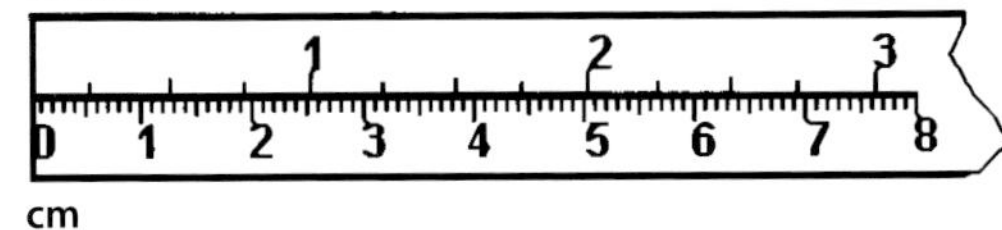